FALCON

FALCON

At the Court of Siam

JOHN HOSKIN

ASIA BOOKS

Published and Distributed by
Asia Books Co. Ltd.,
5 Sukhumvit Road Soi 61,
PO Box 40,
Bangkok 10110,
Thailand.
Tel: (66) 0-2715-9000 ext. 3202–4
Fax: (66) 0-2714-2799
E-mail: information@asiabooks.com
Website: www.asiabooks.com <http://www.asiabooks.com>

This book is a work of fiction.

Front cover illustration courtesy of Old Maps & Prints Co., Ltd.

Typeset by COMSET Limited Partnership
Printed by Darnsutha Press Ltd.

ISBN 974-8303-52-7

For
Ruby, Maya, and Anna

Prologue
The Siamese city of Louvo
18th May, 1688

The sun had barely risen above the tops of the palms and the day was already hot. It would be another few weeks before the long summer months were over and the rains arrived to cool tempers roused by the unrelenting heat.

The morning market crowds were thinning, leaving the poorest townsfolk to haggle over the last of the day's fish, broken eggs, and the limp scraps of vegetables and fruit. Vendors rose stiffly from their haunches and loosened their sarongs before wrapping them more tightly around their waists as they prepared to go home. Dogs, too cowardly or too lazy to bother before, closed in on the leftovers, snarling and snapping at each other.

From the cloudless sky, a hot rush of air swept over the city, tumbling the banana leaves spread over the now empty market stalls, and whipping the edges of their canvas awnings. A group of fishermen returning from the river broke off their conversation to turn their faces from the swirling clouds of dust swept up by the wind, exceptional at this time of year and a bad omen in the superstitious minds of the Siamese.

As if blown by the same wind, a messenger hurried down the street, pushing aside the fishermen and vendors. The people stopped and turned to stare at this man dressed in the red and gold livery of a Royal Servant, wondering what could be so urgent that he rushed on such a hot morning when a slower pace and less agitated mien would be more fitting to his office and his well-being. They watched as he reached the high stone walls of the only large house in the street and pounded at the wooden door behind which a child's laughter was heard.

In the Siamese city of Louvo, second in magnificence only to the Capital Ayutthaya, all the ordinary dwellings were of wood and thatch. Only the temples and the Palace were granted the permanence of stone. So the three grand brick buildings that rose behind these walls awed the townsfolk. They called it Wichayen's House, although the King built it not just for his favourite but also for the Foreign Ambassadors and their Catholic priests who had their own church here. The square European windows and pointed Persian doorways made the house appear even more alien, and only the lotus decoration on the columns struck a familiar note. The Siamese, however, begrudgingly admired the wealth and power symbolized in the palatial proportions of the building, even if most of them despised its foreign occupant.

The door opened and slammed shut as soon as the messenger passed through. The laughter of the child stopped.

"There's trouble, I'll be bound," remarked a fat old woman in an orange and green sarong as she waddled between the empty stalls. She turned and grinned at her young niece who accompanied her, baring teeth blackened by years of chewing betel. "I tell you, as sure as the sunrise, we won't be seeing much more of His Lordship."

For the past three years she had seen Lord Wichayen entertain Foreign Ambassadors and dignitaries, and thought so much nonsense of their haughty ways, their feathered hats and gold embroidered clothes, not to mention fawning priests continually mouthing their god's will in Perpetual Insult to the Lord Buddha.

"Why? Is Lord Wichayen to leave us?" asked the young girl. "They do say he may become king."

"King! Bah. He's a foreigner—lying, cheating, thieving like they all are. He's not to be leaving us as you mean it, nay, but it's my guess he'll lose his head before the next full moon. I hear Phra Petracha and the Mandarins are after his blood, King's Favourite or no King's Favourite."

"But he's so charming and generous. And brave. They still talk down in Ayutthaya about how he fought like a tiger against those horrible Makassars two years past. Besides, he's wondrous different from other foreigners; so familiar with our ways."

"Aye, too familiar. Tell me, if he bows to our King and to Lord Buddha and knows us so well, why's he been fawning on those Frenchmen, wooing them morn, noon, and night? He can't think much of us when he flaunts them fancy foreigners before our eyes. Nay, I tell you, he's rotten. Well, they've all deserted him. He won't last long now. And that'll be a blessing."

"Maybe, Auntie. But I think he's a better gentleman than most of them at Court, what with the old King on his deathbed and all those lazy Mandarins impatient for him to draw his last. It seems only Lord Wichayen stays true to our King. Say what you like, I think he's a mind to become our next monarch."

"Bah, my girl, you must have your head in the clouds," the old woman called over her shoulder as she moved off, turning her back on the Wichayen House.

Lord Wichayen.
The King's Favourite.
Monsieur Constantine.
The Greek.
Phaulkon.

Phaulkon was playing with his young son in the garden of his house when the messenger's pounding at the gate silenced the little boy who was given back to the care of his nurse. Phaulkon retired indoors to receive his impetuous caller.

The breathless messenger entered in an embarrassed rush, pulled his cap from his head, and prostrated himself. He looked up and stared at Phaulkon dressed in a long green robe tied at the waist and seated impassively on a gilded chair. He saw a man of medium height, with straight black hair and handsome rounded features that, had he known, belied years of hardship. Though Phaulkon's countenance was pleasing, his air of cultivation failed to mask an odd brooding expression, as if he were worrying at some plan. A fire burned fiercely within him.

The messenger had heard that this powerful Courtier had once been a cabin boy aboard an English merchantman, though so many stories were told of Phaulkon he knew not what to believe.

"Sire, Phra Petracha has taken the Palace. Although the King is unharmed, his mind has been poisoned. Petracha forced an Audience at His Majesty's bedside and warned that you plotted to seize the throne, thus hiding his treason by dishonouring your name."

Phaulkon said nothing. He slumped in his chair and stared blankly until the messenger, fearful of the silence, withdrew from the room. A moment later, Maria entered the chamber and, seeing her husband's troubled countenance, placed her hand on his arm. He looked into her calm face and, controlling his anger, told her that Phra Petracha had taken command of the Palace, and that the King, although still alive, was a virtual prisoner of this Siamese nobleman.

"Phra Petracha speaks of my treason, when it is he who would be king. I seek only to serve." Phaulkon rose and paced the room, his eyes blind to the rich tapestries, the Persian rugs, the crimson cushions, the fabric of extraordinary wealth that now meant nothing.

Constantine Phaulkon was a man of action. He was obsessed. He swept aside Maria's plea to escape to Bangkok and seek the protection of the French garrison. Though he feared for her safety and that of their child, he believed his Destiny lay with the King. He led her to the chapel and bid her pray with him.

"I commend my fate to you, Our Lord in Heaven. May this day grant me success or that I meet my death with honour."

Rising from the altar, Phaulkon turned to his wife but he could find no words of solace. There was no fear in him, only speechless anger.

He stared long into Maria's eyes, and it was she who at last spoke. "Go, it is God's Will. Let his Will be done. Now hurry to the King who has loved you.

Phaulkon kissed Maria on the cheek and said softly, "It is true that the King has loved me, as I have loved him. But it is you, in your deepest faith, who has given me the Greatest Love. If I have squandered this priceless gift, I beg your forgiveness." He turned swiftly and walked out of the chapel.

After discarding his comfortable robe for boots, breeches, and leather jerkin more practical for a fight, he summoned three French officers to accompany him.

The sun was high as Phaulkon set out for the Palace. A young boy rummaging among the market refuse looked up and would greet this proud foreigner with fire in his eyes, but the man passed quickly by, unseeing.

1

The sunlight, reflected off the still water of the bay, hurt the boy's eyes as he walked out from under the shade of the plane trees, away from the rocky path and down to the beach. The brightness was so intense that for a moment he could not see, and he had to stop and shield his eyes with his hands so he could stare at the four merchant vessels riding at anchor fifty yards offshore.

Even on overcast days, the sight was dazzling enough to these young eyes. The weather never mattered to the boy; winter or summer he would leave off the chores at his parents' inn when no one was watching, and come to the harbour to look at the ships being readied for sea. Always, his heart would beat faster as he saw the bare masts and spars clothed in canvas, and heard the officers bark out their orders in voices of command that boomed across the water. Then came the exquisite moment when the sails filled and one of the traders would slip her moorings and head out of the bay, away from the wretched island.

Perhaps every child has a dream, a desire that is so intensely felt and yet so agonizingly impossible of being grasped, or even fully understood. It was that way for the boy; the ships were like a magnet, drawing him down to the water's edge, and he had no more control over his actions than if he had been sleepwalking. The oddity was that he never wanted to be a sailor, like Alex and some of the other boys in the village. While they stared in admiration at the crewmen who sometimes drank at his parents' inn, he thought these rough men with their gnarled hands and faces tanned like hides were crude and stupid. But they belonged to a ship, and that, to his child's mind, gave them power and freedom. Only much later did he learn that they had neither power nor freedom at all, and were as cruelly treated as they were cruel among themselves. But their ships sailing out to the open sea . . . that was power, freedom, opportunity.

The boy, Constantine Gerakis, had no power and no hope of opportunities opening up before him when he should become a man, and he thought only of escape from this Ionian island of Cephalonia, the place of his birth where he had never known a sense of belonging. Never could he have found contentment on that island which for more than 150 years had been ruled by the Venetians, with whom the local nobles connived, their treachery rewarded with paltry privileges while the ordinary islanders were left to fish or to farm the rocky mountain slopes where nothing but the hardiest trees and vines grew. There were only a few of the island people who had the courage to escape to sea, sustained in their flight either by the hopes of emigrants or by the expectations of traders.

Constantine's mother, however, was proud. "Your father's ancestors were Venetians," she reminded him at every opportunity. "We're important here. You have no need to hang your head and dream of faraway lands," she would say as she went about the daily drudgery of keeping the inn, her patched skirts raising dust whenever she spun round to fling a comment at the boy. "Don't just sit here sulking. Do something useful."

He would fetch and carry, try to be a good son, and then at the first opportunity he would flee the overbearing boredom of the home in which he was supposed to be proud, and find refuge in the sight of the ships that did look proud riding at anchor.

Usually he only stood and stared, returning to the inn when his mother called, but the day came when he didn't heed the summons and instead continued to walk further away, up along the shore. Wandering past the white and red fishing boats drawn up on the sand, their high prows and stems giving them a exaggeratedly concave appearance, he reached the cliffs where the children were forbidden to play because of the swallow holes which, they were told, would suck them down if they fell into the sea. He stood mesmerized by the sight of the water being gulped deep down into the subterranean tunnels that led no one knew where. They made him think of his own youthful passage in life, and where it would lead. Nowhere, he thought, for he had the promise of neither emigrant nor merchant because the Gerakis family—the Falcons, as the name translated—were not birds of the air but innkeepers. And it was a lowly trade at that, in spite of his father's doubtful claims to Venetian lineage. But his parents could never see they were no better off than the farmers and fishermen; could never admit that the hardship of their lives was no different. Why were they so proud? Where did it get them? Many years were to pass before he realized it was his own pride that made him question and quest after a goal he could never define.

From the swallow holes he returned along the beach and looked again out at the bay, seeing a new arrival, an English merchantman easing down the channel in the lee of the tongue of land to the west that made the port of Argostoli a safe haven.

"Fine ships, those. They say some of these English now sail to the Orient, to fabulous cities lit at night by the glow of rubies, and where a man can make his fortune if he's got but half his wits about him." An old fisherman, his weatherbeaten face as dark and wrinkled as a Cephalonian raisin, sat in the shade of one of the beached boats and, like the boy, was staring out to sea.

He turned and looked up at Constantine and seemed to sense the boy's misery. "What are you so down in the mouth for, lad? It's a glorious sight you see here."

"It is only a sight, Sir. Nothing that I can touch to give me happiness."

"Oh, and where would you touch your happiness?"

"Far away, in one of those cities lit by rubies, as you tell. If only I could escape."

"Escape. . . ? Run away, you mean? Well, I suppose you can run from here, get away on one of them ships. Then what? You'll still be you, chaffing at the bit, not knowing where it is you're going. You can't escape, not from yourself. The thing is, son, to know what you really desire. And once you know it, stick with it no matter what others may say. See, that's the curse of this place. Old fellow what founded us, King Kefalos, let himself be made doubtful of all that he loved and desired. It was like this: he had a wife, Prokris, whom he loved dearly. But he was loved by another, a jealous goddess who told him his wife would betray him. 'I'll prove it to you,' said the goddess. 'Disguise yourself as a stranger and try to seduce Prokris with gifts.' Kefalos foolishly did as he was bidden and Prokris gave herself up to the man she thought a stranger. Later, realizing her disloyalty, she fled the island in despair, while Kefalos was a broken man. He had lost everything because he mistrusted and let his faith be weakened."

"That is only more sadness," said the boy when the fisherman finished his tale.

"Maybe there is sadness, but it holds a lesson. Keep faith with what you believe. If you have a dream, then let nothing, not even a goddess, tempt you from your path."

"Sir, I must go. My mother will be calling me."

But Constantine didn't go home. He wandered off to the harbour and stayed there all afternoon, thinking about the old man's story. He watched the English sailors loading wooden crates and sacks and barrels on to the lighters that ferried them out to the merchantman in the bay. Men sweated and cursed and laughed.

"Come on, son, lend us a hand," a muscular young sailor called out to Constantine, but the boy was embarrassed and pretended he had not heard. He sat and stared when no one was paying him attention, mesmerized by a scene that night after night had filled his dreams. In those dreams he would see himself on a ship gazing at a horizon that suddenly unfolded with a landfall at an exotic kingdom in which riches were his for the taking.

Hunger gnawed at his stomach, but still he did not move from the harbour. Darkness fell and the ship's crew, their toil completed, were lighting up their pipes and moving off in groups. One of the English officers who had been overseeing the loading of the cargo looked at Constantine and asked if he had no home to go to.

"Me, Sir? No, Sir?" He didn't know why he lied, but he was never to regret that he did.

"Then have you a mind to join us. We're a cabin boy short."

The words of the old fisherman echoed in the boy's mind, and he needed think only for a moment. "Yes, Sir. A cabin boy would suit if you truly mean the offer."

"Right! Look lively then."

In the few steps to the ship's boat, Constantine vanished from Cephalonia. It was now dark and the rising wind put white crests on the waves. Later, his father came to the port looking for him, but by that time he was fixing up the hammock he had been given in the forecastle, and his ship had already sailed beyond the Ionian Sea and out into wide waters.

It was 18th May, 1658.

At this time, Constantine Phaulkon was 11 years old. The Falcon of Cephalonia had taken wing, but many years would pass before he tasted the wealth and more especially the power that he hungered after.

They were years of hardship and abuse in which only his Ambition and obsession with his Destiny remained undefeated and kept him from taking his own life. That Ambition and obsession would

5

one day cause his name to be uttered variously in tones of fear, admiration, and contempt at Royal Courts on two continents.

φ

Four weeks after sailing from Cephalonia, the young Constantine landed in London. The ship he had escaped on became his home and school, as did the many other English merchantmen in which the boy would serve throughout young manhood.

That first voyage had been an education. Away from family and among men for the first time, Constantine was initially fearful of his rough and unmannered shipmates (how often at his parent's inn had he heard his mother complain of the uncouth English sailors). He had learned generosity and hospitality, however, and that served him well as a cabin boy, and he waited on his shipmates with an ingratiating manner. Languages came easily to him, and the broken English he picked up in just a few days would be quickly perfected. In his enthusiasm to learn and practice a new language, he found he had a lively wit and imagination and could amuse his shipmates with stories about the life and people on Cephalonia, many of which were truthful. In this way he won friends and began to forget his fears.

The ship's officers were pleased with the boy and approved of the diligent way he carried out his duties. But for some of the men it was too diligent.

"It don't do, son, to turn your hand too quick to the bosun's call. You'll be showing us all up," a brute of a sailor once warned the boy, a vicious scar twisting his mouth into a snarl as he spoke.

That evening, still smarting from the sailor's rebuke, Constantine, out of sight of the cook, spat in the man's food before he carried it from the galley and served it.

φ

Twenty years passed. During the brief spells ashore, Constantine lived in the mean streets of London's docks, which were more crowded and the air harder to breath than in a merchantman's forecastle, and it was lucky that he was rarely without a ship, usually finding a berth on one of the English traders plying the Mediterranean ports. In 1672, he served in Prince Rupert's Fleet against the Dutch, and acquitted himself well as an assistant gunner so that shortly afterwards his new master took him East, to India. It was there that he became known as Phaulkon when the ship's officers anglicized his family name Gerakis.

Along with a new name, he acquired in the East a more intense lust to his Ambition as fresh possibilities presented themselves to him. He saw that fortunes could be made in the trade of common nails and hardware, sold in exchange for silks and all manner of exotic goods. He discovered the enormous power and independence of the Eastern trader who could exert authority over lesser men. To grasp these opportunities, he knew he had to better himself. Never short on initiative, he did not waste his time at sea, and had built up a store of knowledge that he would draw on later. He had learnt the art of seamanship, the skills to slip his tongue around outlandish languages, the understanding to appreciate the strange ways of Asian Politics and Manners, and the wit to follow the Byzantine Manner in which those Eastern lands were ruled, and how a clever man could meet what they demanded and reap what they promised.

Rich in knowledge, however, the material gain and the power it might bring, which daily he hungered for, still eluded him. When he returned to Europe he became convinced his future lay in the East and, finding no better position, he signed on for the last time as an ordinary seaman aboard a ship bound for Bantam, the European trading station in Java.

In outposts of trade, it was possible for an ambitious and determined man to rise above the common lot of white flotsam adrift in the Eastern Seas. A change of fortune could come as often by chance as by courage, though the latter was needed in order to grasp the other. It was on 29th May, in the year 1678, the Birthday of King Charles II of England, that Phaulkon, having abandoned the sea and become a junior clerk with the English East India Company in Bantam, took his Fate into his own hands.

For some weeks he had felt demeaned and frustrated by the endless drudgery of ledgers and letters, senseless tasks that he found less to his liking than being deckhand aboard ship. Nor could he see how and where his luck would change. His mood was no better when he awoke on this humid morning in late May. It was stiflingly hot and he had no mind to celebrate, nor the taste for festivities, although he did acknowledge his debt to England, and he had sympathy for King Charles II, a man on whom Fortune had smiled, taking him from exile to a Triumphant Return to the Throne of England, and so Phaulkon was agreeable to be a spectator at the day's celebrations.

He went to stand outside the clerks' room, sheltering in the shade of the roof eaves, and stared idly around the Company's compound watching the ill-disciplined garrison preparing the cannon for the customary Salute in honour of the King. "Buffoons and drunkards, the lot of them," Phaulkon thought to himself. "I despise you all." The gunners must have been toasting Charles II since breakfast, so befuddled with drink did they appear as they scurried about, buttoning up their tunics and readying the guns for the Salute.

Phaulkon's mind drifted away from the scene, and he was wondering where he would be when next the King's Birthday came around. Suddenly a scream of "Fire!" shook him from his reverie. At first he thought it was the order for the Salute, but quickly he realized the word had been uttered in fear not command. He looked across the compound and saw the gun crew running in disarray, yelling and pointing at a burst powder keg that one of them in his drunkenness had managed to set alight while the cannon was being loaded. The flames were almost upon the whole magazine stacked with powder and shot.

Realizing the danger, the men fell into a blind panic and scattered in all directions as the blaze roared out of control. Phaulkon saw that flight was useless. If the flames reached the magazine, all would perish in the explosion. Half the soldiers were running, the other half staring at the flames, too petrified to move. Phaulkon ran across the grounds and darted between the flames into the magazine and hurled away the kegs nearest the fire. His frantic yells startled life into a huddle of terrified natives, and with their help he succeeded in moving all the powder barrels to safety. They then tackled the flames, and soon the fire was brought under control.

And so, on Charles II's Birthday, Phaulkon saved the English East India Company's factory in Bantam from destruction. In reward for his Courage and Quick Action—begrudgingly admitted by his superiors—he was given 1,000 crowns. Never in his life had he set eyes upon such a sum of money. It may not have been a fortune, but it would suffice to make his own if only he used it wisely.

He seized the opportunity, and with his money safely concealed in his clothing, Phaulkon departed the East India Company for good, leaving Bantam aboard a ship bound for Siam, where he intended to enter trade on his own account.

Ayutthaya, Kingdom of Siam
23rd September, 1678

I have arrived in Ayutthaya as one among countless foreigners seeking their fortunes. Portuguese, Dutch, English, French . . . honest men, liars, brave men, cowards, intelligent men, and fools from across half of Europe. Never before have so many Europeans crowded to this Gilded City of the Orient, Capital of Siam, the most powerful Kingdom in Southeast Asia: merchants from Europe's greatest trading houses; missionaries blessed of God; adventurers, thieves, and mercenaries empowered only by their own cunning and greed in the great game of chance where winner takes all.

I have heard some officers of the East India Company living at Ayutthaya claim that the city is as big as London, and estimate the population to be in the order of one million. A French missionary thinks it larger than Paris, with a river three times as broad as the Seine. But to those of us who know the Great Cities of Europe, size is the only familiar element, and everything else appears strange and fabulous.

Nothing compares. Other Oriental trading posts I have seen at Ban-tam or Fort St. George at Madras are modelled in the European like-ness. But Ayutthaya is utterly singular. It is a Fantastic Concoction; a labyrinth unknown to the European mind, over which a King rules as a Lord of Life surrounded by a Court more Glorious than even that of Old Byzantium. And like Byzantium, it is a place of intrigue, of struggles for power and influence, of rivalry and romance. Any man, or woman—for the fair sex, too, can be powerful and cunning—who is driven by ambition or love, need keep their wits about them and know the measure of others. As spectacle, Ayutthaya rivals the Glory of the Sun King at Versailles under whose rays France basks.

It is, nonetheless, a hidden world, and though ships can sail to the very walls of the city, they approach from the Gulf of Siam—some 15 leagues to the south—only via the Menam River, which assures that no arrival ever comes unannounced or uninvited. From the river's mouth, guarded by a great bar of mud, ships sail past Paknam, which is nothing more than a collection of bamboo huts, and on to Bangkok where there is a fort and a customs post. Here, vessels must wait until permission is granted for them to continue their journey. Boats moving upstream navigate between lush green banks where thick tropical vegetation reaches down to the water's edge. In clearings away from the stands of coconut and areca palms laden with fruit, the fertile flood plains are covered with rice paddy, which in season adds an emerald hue to the rich greens of Nature. Livening this placid scene can be seen monkeys and all manner of birds, while villages of wood and bamboo houses raised high on stilts appear at intervals, and the playful cries of children splashing in the shallows echo across the water.

Suddenly the tranquil countryside recedes and there stands Ayutthaya. Only then do the Europeans catch their breath at the sight of Siam's Capital City, mysterious and Resplendent, full of promise and peril.

The city is strong and great, seated upon an island around which flows a river where ride ships from India, Persia, China, and Japan; from France, Holland, and England; while innumerable sampans laden with fruit jostle for space in the crowded market areas, and on the wider waterways golden barges rowed by sixty men glide sedately to and fro. Stone walls two leagues in circumference surround the city, which is shaped like a purse, the mouth lying to the east and the bottom to the west. The river meets it at the north by several channels, which run into the encircling ring of water, and leaves it on the south by separating itself again into several channels. The streets, stretching out of sight, are alleys of water.

Ayutthaya is indeed the Venice of the Orient. Nay, finer than Venice for if the buildings are not so grand, the canals are very long, very straight, and deep enough to carry the largest vessels, so that these labyrinthine waterways are no mere fancy but greatly facilitate transport and provide irrigation for the fields. Water further affords safety and protection, making it difficult to lay siege to the city whose surrounding plains are flooded during the season of rains so that no army can advance by land.

On the north of the island stands the King's Palace, enclosed by a double wall of brick, about half a league in circumference. Within are several courtyards of varying size, as well as elephant stables designed in grandness according to the Rank and Dignity of the animals that reside in them. In the first two courtyards are the lodgings of the officials of the Royal Household, while in others are various old apartments of former kings, which are accorded reverence as Sacred Places and where avenues of trees make it pleasant enough to walk. The King's Apartment is in the last courtyard, easily distinguished by the gold that glitters all over it in a thousand places. It is in the form of a Cross, in the middle of which there rises from the roof a Many-Tiered Pyramid. All sides are adorned with carving of the very best workmanship, while the windows look out to spacious, well-tended gardens.

Outside the Palace, the riverbank is to the left, where the great boat-houses shelter more than 150 Royal Barges, each and every one richly adorned. Back from the river is a large park, and it is here that the Royal Family views the taming of wild elephants, beasts so important to the Siamese that every aspect of their capture and keep is steeped in lore.

The quarter of the city where the ordinary Siamese live is so densely populated that it can easily supply the King with 60,000 men of age to bear arms. There are also a great many artisans here: woodcarvers, silversmiths, metal workers, potters, weavers. Many of the numerous streets are dedicated to a single craft. There are spacious squares where markets are held at dawn and dusk, when the throng of people is so great one can hardly push one's way through. Some of the roads are laid with brick, others are unpaved, while most are lined with fine trees that provide welcome shade, for it is intolerably hot at all hours.

In this Oriental Venice, the streams and canals are crossed by many bridges, a half dozen of which are splendid affairs of arched brickwork, though others are made of bamboo and are so rickety that it is difficult to cross them without fear of falling into the water.

If the houses of the commoners are made simply of teak and thatch sitting on stilts above the livestock stabled beneath, what makes Ayutthaya such a wondrous place to behold is the panorama of over 500 temples, standing on all sides like golden pyramids with soaring spires and gilded eaves winking in the sunlight.

Away from the Native Quarter is another district of the city that is assigned to foreigners—Chinese and Mohammedans, as well as Europeans. Crowded and full of substantial houses, many built of brick, this is the Commercial Heart of Ayutthaya. All vessels berth here, and the river forms a wide basin suitable for repairing ships. There are shipyards too, and every day new vessels are launched.

Around Ayutthaya lie many villages, some consisting entirely of moored boats; beyond are wide rice fields, while the horizon is of tall trees, above which are visible the curling roofs and tapering spires of more temples. A French Jesuit told me he has never seen a view lovelier than the scene presented by the city. It is possible his Mischievous Wit gets the better of him, or, like the Siamese, he tells what he thinks others would like to hear, for beautiful though

Ayutthaya is, I must be honest and say none of us suffered the months at sea only to admire the view.

What truly gladdens all our eyes is the constant stream of trade, and the wealth it promises. Ships from China and Japan bring silk, tea, porcelain, quicksilver, and bronze, taking away in return scented woods, pepper, hides, and edible bird's nests—a delicacy for which the Chinese have a rare fondness. Since neither Indian and Persian ships sail all the way to China and Japan, nor Chinese and Japanese ships voyage direct to India, Ayutthaya finds itself in the middle, richly placed to reap the ripe fruit that geography has so fortuitously dropped in its lap. As the Siamese scorn the toil of commerce, if not its rewards, the situation satisfies all. None more so than King Narai, who retains a Royal Monopoly on all commerce, and is possessed of a vision that holds more for Siam than any monarch has imagined before him.

Occupying the Throne for these past 22 years, King Narai has pursued greater relations with foreigners than any of his predecessors. Japan and China may fear the Europeans and close their ports to Christians. Narai believes otherwise, and sees progress as dependent on taking the good from the European example while keeping a check on the bad. In seeking Siam's Greater Glory, he charts a middle passage between East and West. He is Siam's Glory, and the very thread by which it so delicately hangs.

Narai reigns as Lord of Life over his subjects. The strangeness of his Court and the splendour of his Royal Entourage are unseen before by Europeans who, despite kings of our own, can find comparison to such glory only in Biblical accounts of the pharaohs or of Solomon. Enthroned in his walled Palace, where he takes counsel from his Brahmin astrologers, the King appears, to the few permitted to his presence, like some pagan idol. Mandarins, Ministers, Princes, and Petitioners prostrate themselves on knees and elbows in the Audience Chamber, empty save for three tiered umbrellas at the far wall. Below the central umbrella is a curtain; trumpets and drums are sounded and the curtain is drawn aside to reveal the Monarch, lofty and remote, dressed in red and gold and wearing a tall, tapering tiara flashing diamonds, rubies, and sapphires. It is the vision of a god, and at the moment of revelation the assembled Mandarins rise on their knees and, hands placed together as if in prayer, bow their foreheads to the ground three times.

Godlike, too, is the King when he travels abroad mounted on an elephant. At four o'clock in the afternoon, foot soldiers with helmets, breastplates, and gilded shields, and horseguards of Indian Mohammedans—each a splendid fellow; strong, tall, and proud—close off the streets. Mandarins march before and behind the King, each wearing his hat of ceremony, shaped like a pyramid with rings of gold denoting Rank. But the commoners are not permitted on to the streets, nor to peer from their windows, and bamboo screens strewn with flowers maintain an illusion of the Divine.

Showered with the radiance of its Monarch, Ayutthaya is rich and powerful—and vulnerable. Siam's power to attract is also its weakness. To a King freed from his predecessors' burden of wars on the western border, the luxury to indulge new-sought alliances is irresistible. But who is to say which be friend or foe? The nations of Europe squabble among themselves, vying for advantages in trade. The Portuguese are a spent force, but the Dutch are strong and experienced in the East, jealous rivals to all who seek their own trade. The English present a challenge, and the French—new players in this game—have yet to reveal their hand, other than as missionaries. Any of these could be valuable partners in trade; all could be a dangerous enemy if gaining the upper hand. In such a climate, it seems to me, a clever man who gains the King's ear could broker alliances and be king himself in all but name.

From the first moment I set eyes on Ayutthaya, I am convinced my Destiny lies here. My thoughts, my imagination, my thirst for knowledge all draw me deeper into the city, and each day during my first weeks here I have roamed the streets and taken sampans along the canals and out on the river that bristles with the masts of ships of all nations. I am awed and feel as if it is only now that I am truly awake for the first time in my life. Here is everything I hunger after. All I need is the opportunity.

2

Phaulkon spent his first months in Siam making himself familiar with his new surroundings, and was tireless in exploring the city, getting to know the ways of trade and those engaged in it. On a fine morning, pleasant now that the cool season was well set in, he was passing by the factory of the East India Company when a voice hailed him in the street.

"Constantine Phaulkon, isn't it?"

He looked about him and saw a man approaching whom he recognized as Richard Burnaby, the officer in charge of the English Company's affairs at Ayutthaya. He had travelled with him from Bantam to Siam, but so far had had little dealing with him. He was confronted by an amiable man of middling stature and fair enough put together, but he had a weakness about the mouth, and the set of his jaw indicated no strong will. He was, for all that, a man of

influence, and Phaulkon was delighted to make his acquaintance—
flattered that he should be sought out in this fashion.

"I'm Burnaby, with the English Company here, as you probably
know," Burnaby introduced himself. "I've heard much about you
and have been seeking a chance to meet. Come, if you have the time,
let us take a stroll. There's someone I'd like you see."

The two fell in together and walked in the shade of the trees. For
a while the conversation was no more than an exchange of pleasantries, although Phaulkon sensed there was some hidden design in
Burnaby's talk, and that he had yet to speak his true thoughts. After
they had walked some way, the senior man turned and looked at
Phaulkon. "Forgive my bluntness, Sir," he said, "but, you know, I've
a feeling we could make your fortune."

The Englishman had an abrupt way of speaking, and Phaulkon
first thought he was making a bold attempt to recruit him back into
the services of the Company.

Burnaby quickly corrected him. "No, no, my dear Phaulkon. The
Company is finished here, of that I've no doubt. There is nothing
more I can do. All my efforts have been in vain—London simply
does not listen. No, the only way is to be in business for yourself . . .
become an Interloper as the Company men are wont to call free
trade. Come in with me and George White, whom you must have
heard of. We have our little business established and we need an independent agent. We can help you out with a ship and cargo."

It seemed an improbable offer. Yet Phaulkon had nothing to lose.
What else had he? He was 31 years old and could yet claim no higher
standing in the world than that of ordinary seaman and junior clerk
become modest trader. He was surprised at Burnaby singling him
out from all the other opportunists drawn to Ayutthaya, yet he
flattered himself that certain qualities of his might not have gone
unnoticed during the short time he had been in Siam's Capital. In
those early days of trying to establish himself as an independent
trader, he had discovered an unbounded energy and a facility to
ingratiate himself easily with people who might be of use to him,

while they in turn noticed his quickness to learn and his talent for languages. He made no effort to hide his Ambition to better himself. So he was pleased when he learned that the Dutch Agent for Siam had joked that so industrious was he that no sooner was he seen in one place than he was heard of in another. He had a temper, and his Greek pride never allowed him to forget an insult, but these traits he contained for the most part.

As they talked, the two men strolled along a brick-laid path running beside a canal overhung with flame trees. Ayutthaya had many such areas, like gardens, that offered shade and were sparsely peopled, so conversations could be held without fear of being overheard by spies in the pay of Siamese nobles, or foreign trade agents ever mindful of competition.

Burnaby did most of the talking while Phaulkon listened, attentive but careful to show no sign of the growing enthusiasm he felt for the proposition the Englishman outlined. Their walk brought them to the house of George White.

"The only honest rogue in the Eastern Seas and my partner in trade, George White . . . Mister Constantine, otherwise Phaulkon the Greek, the most energetic man in all of Siam." Burnaby made the effusive introductions.

The man Phaulkon saw was perhaps thirty, a year or so younger than himself. He wore breeches and a jacket like a sleeved waistcoat, and he appeared a Gentleman. As he stood in the doorway, holding out his hand in welcome, a broad smile lit up his kindly face. "I think, Sir, we have met before."

"Indeed, Sir, you are most kind," Phaulkon replied. "You are correct. It was serving aboard the *Hopewell* on the voyage from London to Madras some eight years ago. I remember well you were among our company, but I am honoured that you should have noticed such a lowly seaman as me."

"Man, how could I not notice one so clearly with his mind set on making his fortune," White exclaimed. "In those brooding eyes of yours, I saw a restless soul. So now you have finally quit the sea and forsaken London for Siam?"

"Let us not say 'forsaken.' As an Englishman, Sir, you must know that in that Kingdom I breathed for the first time after my infancy an air I had tasted no sweeter until brought to this place. I do not forsake London, though I most heartedly embrace Siam."

"Gentlemen, gentlemen," called Burnaby. "It is well that you two be acquainted, but we are not here to remember the past but to seal our futures. Come, let us advise our dear Phaulkon of our plans." White invited the men into his house and, seating them at a teak-wood table, he summoned his servant to bring brandy.

The house was light and spacious, though not grandly furnished, and Phaulkon suspected White was a careful man, living frugally while increasing his business. He had heard that Burnaby had invited him to help sort out the Company affairs, and in that Burnaby had showed good judgement, for White had a reputation as a shrewd man of affairs and an upright man, too, for all his being an Interloper in the India Trade.

After toasting each others' health, Burnaby continued his explanations: "As you must have heard, I was posted to Ayutthaya to sort out the tangled affairs of the East India Company. What I found was utter disorder: no proper accounts, quarrels between the staff, money borrowed from the Siamese King on the Company's security for private trade, and even our stock of English broadcloth is quite unsaleable. Chaos. It was then that I enlisted the help of George, here. But we can both see the Company is a broken reed and that we'd be better served by serving ourselves.

"As you well know, Phaulkon, the Company's Royal Charter allows no one outside its own members to trade in the East. A merchant bold enough to set out on his own account as a free trader is at once damned as an Interloper, and yet to be in the Company one must hold capital shares, and those shares rarely come onto the market. They've got a monopoly, and a very lucrative one at that. The odd thing is that we English hate Royal Monopolies, and there are plenty of us who believe the riches of the Eastern Trade should be open to all. There's wealth enough. Now, the problem George and I have is that we're still Company Officials, and that's why we are looking for someone like yourself, Phaulkon, to be our agent and handle our private affairs. What say you?"

Phaulkon was drawn to Burnaby for his openness and optimism, but White, whom he was well pleased to see again, was the better man, and Phaulkon was confident from what he knew of his reputation that he could trust him—and there were few men of whom he could say the same.

"What stake would I need to set up in trade with your kind selves?" Phaulkon replied to the offer.

"All that you have," said Burnaby with a laugh, adding that it was Phaulkon's energy and enthusiasm that counted most, but the more he could invest in trade goods, the greater would be his return.

Phaulkon decided there and then to stake all he owned, every last farthing of the reward he had received at Bantam. Time would tell whether he was a fool or not.

Ayutthaya
19th December, 1679

Tomorrow I embark upon the greatest voyage of my life. And I owe it all to Burnaby and White, especially White who has been most generous with his advice, teaching me much about the ways of trade and about the proper conduct of a Gentleman Merchant.

These past months have been like a dream. My star rises by the day and I move up in the world. Before I was a plain seaman, now I am master of my own small vessel, bought with the assistance of Burnaby and White, both of whom have remained true to their word and have taken me on as an equal partner in trade. And I feel safe in saying, I have been true to my benefactors. I have now made two voyages: one to Achin on the island of Sumatra with a mixed cargo, and another to Japan where I was successful in selling at a handsome profit a consignment of English cloth that could find no market in Siam.

I have discovered that trade comes naturally to me. I have a good head for business, and never tire of pursuing the greatest return on the goods we have to sell. After both of my trips, we poured our gains back into the business to purchase better stock to gain even more profitable trade. For all my life I have endured poverty, and I lust over the wealth I am now beginning to accumulate.

Strangely, I must admit, the lust is never satisfied. It is not only that I want greater profit, but that profit itself does not assuage the hunger in my soul, although I cannot say precisely what I lack, what will make me replete. In all the years since I left Cephalonia I have never forgotten the old fisherman who urged me as a boy to follow the path of my dreams, and while I take pride in serving Burnaby and White diligently, I believe myself worthy of a Greater Calling.

It is, therefore, with some premonition which I cannot define, that I wait eagerly for tomorrow's venture. I say my greatest voyage, though it will be of no great distance; rather it is the gamble that is the greatest I have ever undertaken.

"There's a huge profit to be made in this venture," Burnaby confided in me not two weeks ago. "Though it be a delicate undertaking, demanding a man of your resources and resolve. You will have heard the rumours that rebels in Singora, on the Southern Coast, are plotting against Siamese rule, but they need arming and provisioning if they are to succeed in their plans. This we will do. One small ship with a full cargo, a short voyage under the guise of our usual trade and, yes, a huge profit I think."

I agreed readily to the plan, and paid no mind to its dangers. For the past ten days I have fitted out our small vessel and taken on a hand-picked crew of four. All is now ready and my ship, lying low in the water with her cargo of guns, powder, and provisions, awaits only the morning tide.

3

The sky was clear when Phaulkon boarded his ship early in the morning and he slipped his moorings at Ayutthaya, passing downstream to the customs post and fort at Bangkok without hindrance. Having cleared the bar at the mouth of the river, he set a course due south, mindful to keep well off the coast but within sight of it.

Fair weather held until he was passing Ligor, still some leagues north of his destination. His ship was then overtaken by a storm with that sudden violence as found only in the tropics. The sky darkened, bolts of lightening shot through the black clouds, and a fierce wind raged, whipping up an angry sea of white-crested waves that broke over the sides of the small ship. Phaulkon gave orders for the sails to be taken in, only to see the bare masts snapped by the ferocity of the gale.

Clinging to the helm, Phaulkon managed to keep the vessel upright, riding the storm, until he was rendered helpless when the rudder was torn away in a sudden surge of fury. The stricken vessel took in water at a frightening rate. Phaulkon screamed to the crew above the roar of the wind to throw the guns and powder barrels overboard in a desperate bid to lighten the vessel and keep her afloat. Still the storm had them at its mercy, and, realizing they would never reach the coast, Phaulkon gave orders to abandon ship.

It was not the first time he had been shipwrecked, and he did not panic. He had no fear for his own life; only anguish at how this disaster would surely ruin him as he and his crew clung to planks torn off the wrecked vessel and gave themselves up to the waves that finally threw them exhausted onto the shore.

Phaulkon and his crew had been freed from the fury of the sea only to find themselves at the mercy of the land's hostility. A band of Malays, who had sighted the wreck, swarmed to the water's edge in the hope of finding loot. They quickly found Phaulkon, and seeing him in a state of near collapse from exhaustion, stripped him of all he possessed and left him for dead.

News of the shipwreck was also quick in reaching the Governor of Ligor who, mindful of the rebels at Singora and suspicious of any foreign vessel in these waters, at once ordered a search for survivors. Phaulkon was discovered sheltering in a thicket where he had crawled to hide the shame of his nakedness and despair.

Dragged before the Governor in the rags the search party had seen fit to provide him, Phaulkon saw in the man's fixed stare a more piercing gaze of confrontation than he had ever seen in Siamese eyes—which will usually avoid direct contact in all but the most heated of circumstances. He mustered sufficient presence of mind, however, to return the man's glare, and was fully alert to the fact that he would be fatally compromised if any of the arms or powder from the wreck had been discovered. He pulled his exhausted body erect and maintained a calm countenance.

"You. What business?" snapped the Governor in poor English.

Phaulkon felt the sharpness of the man's tone. His mind flashed back to his hiding naked and distraught at the failure of his mission, despairing at the cruel blow to his Ambition. How could he face his benefactors in Ayutthaya? Yet to return a failure to the island of his birth, even if it were possible, was unthinkable. Death was preferable. Now, shaken by this haughty Governor, a mere provincial lackey for all his local powers, Phaulkon's pride was aroused and he held fast to a belief in himself. Providence would preserve him.

"My Lord," he replied in Siamese, "in what language would you care to conduct this interview. I am proficient in English, Portuguese, Malay, Greek, and your own melodious tongue? Whichever pleases you."

The Governor's eyes widened in surprise when he heard Phaulkon speak Siamese, and speak it well. He believed all Europeans were too ignorant to master his own language. Now he was taken aback, uncertain of himself. Phaulkon could imagine him thinking to himself that he would need to tread cautiously with someone who understood him perfectly in his own language; a person of some learning and obviously acquainted with Siamese ways. But the Governor quickly recovered, and now saw Phaulkon in an even more sinister light because of his ease with the language.

"We will speak Siamese, seeing that you appear oddly to be so familiar with it," the Governor replied. A brief, cynical smile vanished as he returned a hard stare. "You and your crew were making passage to the rebels in Singora. That is so, yes?"

The Governor's bold accusation momentarily shook Phaulkon. "He cannot know the truth. He's guessing," he told himself. Looking straight into the eyes of his inquisitor, and trusting that guilt did not show in his own, he spoke: "No, Sir, you are mistaken. We are but ordinary traders, bearing a mixed cargo bound for Achin."

"Don't insult me! The wreckage was of a small vessel, a coastal trader. Answer me. Your destination was Singora. Your cargo guns. You are a traitor to Siam!"

"No! Respectfully, I repeat My Lord is mistaken. Ours is but honest trade. We know of no rebels, much less support a cause that would harm our Sovereign Lord, King Narai." Phaulkon forced a gentle smile and held his composure, though God knew the fear that was pounding in his heart.

The Governor remained firm in his conviction of Phaulkon's guilt. He maintained a barrage of questions, only to find that Phaulkon was equally sustained in his claim of innocence.

Finally, frustrated with the Greek's guile and smooth tongue and his patience so exhausted, the Governor resigned himself to the fact that Phaulkon had the better of him. His last words to his captive were, "You will, I prophesize, rise to greatness—if you do not lose your head first."

Washing his hands of the matter, the Governor dispatched Phaulkon and his crew to Ayutthaya. In issuing his instructions to his aide, he remarked—forgetting or uncaring that Phaulkon spoke Siamese—"Let the Phra Klang deal with this accursed man ere he deals with us."

Ayutthaya
12th January, 1680

It is before the Barcalon that I am to present myself on my being sent back from Ligor on a Siamese ship. Charged with crimes against Siam, I am ostensibly under arrest, although I have been given the freedom of my own house in Ayutthaya.

The man to whom I am to answer my case has a passion for accumulating riches. Chao Phya Kosa Tibodi, holder of the title Phra Klang, commonly spoken by foreigners as 'Barcalon,' enjoys the Esteem of the King and the people for his many fine qualities. Short, fat, wealthy, and powerful—a man of full weight as the Chinese say—his one weakness is that he can never resist a gift. For many it is a happy flaw to be found in the Minister of the Treasury.

Since King Narai ascended the Throne of Siam in 1656, and recognized the advantages of intercourse with foreigners, trade has been a Royal Monopoly controlled by the Barcalon, one of his four Chief Ministers. All merchants must deal with this man, and as virtually all traders are foreigners, the Barcalon is effectively Foreign Minister as well as Minister of the Treasury, thereby in an enviably unique position to command power and wealth.

If I had but money, I would not fear meeting this man; a bribe I am sure would rid me of all charges against me. But now I have nothing. All was lost in that terrible venture to Singora.

4

Two days after he was brought back to the Siamese Capital, Phaulkon received Burnaby and White at his home. They, like all the other foreign traders, had heard rumours of the Greek's shipwreck and the suspicion that hung over him, and were anxious to learn how badly they all stood in the matter.

Phaulkon was downcast when his servant brought his two bene-factors into the room. He scarcely greeted them as he stared at the floor. Then he gave his account of the disaster, leaving nothing out of his tale of the shipwreck and subsequent interrogation by the Governor of Ligor. "To my shame, Gentlemen, everything is lost. I have no way to recover it," he concluded.

But shame did not sit easily on the shoulders of the Greek. He stood up suddenly, surprising his audience and, as if shaking off a mantle that was weighing him down, squared his shoulders and looked straight at Burnaby and White. "Sirs," he spoke, "I am a prisoner now, but I swear I shall find the means to repay you, may God spare me."

Burnaby glanced at White. Both men were disturbed by their friend's agitated state, although they knew as well as he how grave was the situation. They had sailed close to the wind before; this was different. The undertaking they had entrusted to Phaulkon was illegal, and he had been caught. The Siamese clearly saw a connection between his ill-fated voyage and the rebels at Singora. They would all surely be implicated.

None spoke for several minutes, leaving Phaulkon's words of entreaty to the Divine to wither in the hot, humid air.

It was Burnaby who broke the silence, and what he suggested was so bold, so audacious, so dear to a gambler's heart that Phaulkon saw at once that it was a masterstroke if he could fashion it so.

"We are indeed in a tight corner, Burnaby said, "but through no error of yours, my dear Phaulkon. No blame attaches to you." He paused to smile at his friend and protégé. "But we must outwit our hosts. Kill the suspicion of any wrongdoing on your part, and ours of course, and leave ourselves free to continue trade, perhaps even better placed than we were.

"Your generous offer to repay our investment, Phaulkon, is well received, but no. I think we should invest more," he said with a flourish, tossing a bag of coin on the table.

"This, my dear Phaulkon, you will present with your compliments to His Excellency the Barcalon after I have proposed you as that exalted person's Most Valuable Aide in acting as an interpreter in his dealings with all foreign merchants. After all, you speak the language and know the ways of trade, and you are industrious. Yes, indeed, an invaluable man. And with your gift to open his eyes, the Barcalon will not fail to see your worth."

"By God, Richard, it's perfect!" White clapped his hands in admiration. "Friend Phaulkon here gets off the hook—for who would dare utter suspicions of a man in the Service of Siam—and we have our own man in the Treasury. Brilliant."

Phaulkon could not help smiling at the audacity of Burnaby's plan, and the despair he had felt only moments earlier drained away. To enter the Siamese King's Service would be full of danger, doubly so for a foreigner. On the other hand, the prospects were irresistible.

Phaulkon did not hesitate, and turning to Burnaby, replied, "My Master and Benefactor, I will do as you bid."

Ayutthaya
15th January, 1680

Burnaby's and White's visit has left me much revived in spirits. My Fate hangs on the success of Burnaby's plan, and I now begin to get a deeper insight into the enormous potential Siam can offer a man of intelligence, resource, and courage.

Until this moment, I have been engaged only in trade, yet now I can envisage a political course for myself. Trade has its rewards, but when it remains a Royal Monopoly, and so many nations vie for the profits, any real gain must come from within. I begin to see what sort of role a foreigner could fill in this Kingdom; a vital role if Siam is to accommodate the Europeans, checking one nation with another and so gaining the advantages while avoiding the threat foreign intercourse poses to her Sovereignty.

As my ideas and plans grow in grandeur and audacity—I have little else to do but think while confined to my house—so they become more clearly defined. They go far beyond anything I or any other foreigner has dreamed of before, and yet I believe all is possible, within my grasp. I have the desire for such a role, and the strength of mind to take it. All I possess in this world, together with Burnaby's gift, I will present to the Barcalon, and with the knowledge of that man's weakness, I am confident of securing my future. I will meet the Barcalon, and that man, like Burnaby and White, will be impressed with my capabilities.

Siam in this age is like a courtesan who chooses to remain her own mistress. After almost incessant war with the Burmese, she enjoys unfamiliar Peace and Prosperity. Now she will give herself to those who bring her the greatest riches and the least trouble. Wisely knowing that she has neither the skill, nor the experience, nor even the inclination to soil her hands with commerce, she seeks to exploit her undoubted attractions by selling her favours to others, so long as she retains her Freedom.

In this Year of Our Lord 1680, that freedom is under threat. Siam has given herself up to trade, and though the Royal Monopoly is in force, much profit is lost in the transactions conducted by foreigners. Moreover, by yielding trade to others, Siam lays herself open; her very Sovereignty is in danger.

Trade is of two kinds. One is the exchange of commodities between the East and Europe. The other, what Europeans call Coastal Trade, involves commerce between India and China and Japan, for which Siam is the crossroads. This coastal trade is by tradition in the hands of the Moors, Mohammedans from India and Persia who have settled in Siam.

It has been this way for over 200 years. Now is the time for change.

5

"I could hardly have dreamed it better," Burnaby reported to George White after taking Phaulkon to be introduced to the Barcalon. "He's not a bad old boy as the Siamese go. As usual he kept us standing at the door while he drew on his cheroot, puffing out clouds of smoke. Then he invited us in and offered us chairs, set specially for us before his couch. I could see the shrewd devil was eyeing Phaulkon, trying to get his measure.

"Finally, he made a few pleasantries to me before quizzing our man, asking his name, age, how long he had been in Siam, and how many languages he spoke. And you know what, George, as we expected Phaulkon floored the fellow by replying to all his questions in fluent Siamese. Old Chao Phya Kosa could scarcely believe his ears. I could see how impressed he was. Our friend has an uncanny way of showing due deference without diminishing his own pride. I don't know how he does it."

George White looked pleased at the news, but he did not feel as cocksure as Burnaby obviously was. "And the position, Richard? Did the Barcalon offer to take Phaulkon into service?"

"Of course. Is that not what I'm saying. He offered and Phaulkon could not but accept. I'm telling you, the old boy was delighted. Took him on there and then."

"And what of the charges against our friend over the Singora business?"

"Dismissed. Lack of evidence. The Barcalon expressed his sympathy over Phaulkon's misfortune and wished him better luck in his service."

White turned to the window and stared out across the city of Ayutthaya bleached in the harsh sunlight. "Do you think it will work?"

He was a more serious man than Burnaby, whose sensual interests and indiscreet tongue he distrusted. While at the same time liking him, he sometimes wondered if Burnaby really knew what he was doing. After all, Phaulkon, for all his talents, was a dangerous man—a friend to value, an enemy to fear. White admired him as much as Burnaby did, although he wondered how he would turn out. "I mean to say, Richard, it's the English Trade, our trade that matters.

"Of course. But with a friend at Court we'll have the information and the favours to give us advantage. I hear the King already fears the power of the Dutch, and the English Company, if only we can wake it up, is just the thing to keep a balance. The French, as much as the King courts them, are latecomers. Missionaries. Phaulkon can turn much our way."

"Aye, he might just. Do you trust him?"

"No question. You know yourself he grew up in the Company's employ."

"Not necessarily a good school, he being a foreigner."

"Well, look at what he's done for us. Only a little bad fortune got him unstuck. Besides, he knows this gets him out of that scrape down South. I am certain of his loyalty. He's a good fellow."

"I agree that he's always shown himself loyal to his benefactors—only now, my friend, he may come to find he has more people to please than he can master."

"Come, my friend," said Burnaby, reaching for the brandy flagon. "Join me in a toast to Phaulkon's success. May he serve Siam and us well."

Ayutthaya
9th February, 1680

My first weeks in the service of the Barcalon have been un-eventful but most instructive, and my imagination has been fired as I begin to formulate a plan that will serve me well.

With Burnaby and White, I have been a man of business and, setting aside modesty, I believe I have shown rare aptitude for this. Trade alone, however, may bring riches, but riches alone will never satisfy me. It is well, then, that I now see that the most pressing problems affecting Siam are those of trade. With boldness, courage, and an unflinching nerve, I can, I believe, address these problems.

"Whatever department should suit you, Your Excellency. And as for my salary, I ask for nothing save the Honour of serving His Majesty the King." That was my reply when the Barcalon sum-moned me on my first day and asked in what role I should prefer to serve and what payment I should expect.

For a moment the old man was speechless. Presumably he had never before encountered a petitioner seemingly so heedless of his own gain. Then he rubbed his pudgy fingers across his ample belly and chuckled his delight. Perhaps he thought me a simpleton. For my part, I had already placed him as an amiable fool. He would not have looked so pleased, however, if he knew my thoughts regarding my fortune. Lesser men might name their price, but for me there is no sum that will satisfy. Only power. Have that, and the other is either limitless or meaningless.

"Well, we'll see what we can do, my friend," was all the Barcalon could reply. He rose and, beckoning me to follow, waddled on his short legs to the door, where he summoned a servant to show me the offices. These formed part of a Grand Apartment in the outer courtyard of the Palace, and looked onto lush gardens so full of tropical plants that it was hard to remember we were in the midst of a huge metropolis.

I quickly lost count of the clerks I saw. None appeared to be much occupied, and all stared at me, curious at this foreigner who was to work among them. Nothing was said, only smiles were exchanged, which I knew meant nothing, and I told myself I would need be judicious in choosing allies, and ruthless in exerting what authority I might gain. For all their smiles, the Siamese remain mistrustful of foreigners.

I returned to the Barcalon's Private Chambers, where he dismissed me, saying only that I should make myself familiar with the Trade Department of the Treasury and with the King's Storehouses.

The queries and problems brought by diverse foreign traders that I had to deal with over the following days were easily settled, and I used every minute of my time and every means to learn the ways of Court life in Ayutthaya and the patterns and practices of the considerable business that sustains that life.

In theory, all is simple: the King of Siam is a monarch who commands respect among his neighbours, and wealth at home, the two being not totally divorced from each other, and combined amount to unchallenged power through trade, itself built on the courteous exchanges of Missions between the King and his various counterparts in Achin, Golconda, Persia, and elsewhere.

Trade is everything, for the King demands sole right to the primary acquisition and sale of all manner of commodities, whether it be elephants, scented woods, betel nuts, tin . . . whatever. So anyone who wishes either to sell goods in Siam or to export abroad must purchase from the King. Death being the penalty for abuse of the Royal Monopoly.

The Siamese are not merchants themselves, but such is the manner of trade that the Mandarins manipulate it for both public and private interests; indeed, most officials do not distinguish between the two.

The weakness of the system, as I have come to realize, lies in the fact that the Siamese entrust their trade to those with the requisite means and experience, in this case the Moors. But with regulations most flawed, the Moors make great gain on their own account by trading overseas in goods purchased in Siam from the King. Moreover, when foreign rulers return His Majesty's Favours by sending their own Missions to Ayutthaya, the Moors find another lucrative source of income at the King's Expense by charging exorbitant fees for the arrangements they make for the appropriately Regal Reception and entertainment of these foreign guests.

Such has been the accepted practice for as long as anyone cares to remember, but I have come to believe that the Barcalon is now privately much troubled by the excesses of the Moors. Commissions he expects, even a little pilfering of the profits, but I have discovered the scale of the deficits is so astonishing that before long Siam could effectively be in the service of the Moors rather than the other way round.

Now, if I expose this, will I not rise in the Barcalon's esteem? If only I can find a way to the turn the Moors' loss into my gain.

6

After long having left Phaulkon to his own devices, the Barcalon finally summoned him to his office. He, too, had been contemplating the problem of the Moors, wondering how he could possibly curb their activities, worried as much that it was his profits and not just the King's that were suffering. At length he decided, without great optimism, that he would test his new assistant and place him in charge of a Foreign Mission instead of allowing it to the Moors.

"Phaulkon. Now that you have had time to see the workings of My Office and you, as has been well recommended to me, are a man truly versed in the art of sea trade, it is desirous that you conduct a Mission of His Majesty's Envoys to . . . er . . ." the Barcalon fumbled with some documents on his table to find the name of the country to be honoured with King Narai's Representatives . . . "Persia. Yes, Persia. Would you be able to acquit yourself in this manner?"

"Your Excellency, should it be your wish, I would be honoured to take upon myself this Mission in the name of our Beloved King," Phaulkon replied without hesitation. Only later did he admit to Burnaby that he was daunted by the sudden turn of events, knowing that the Envoys on such Missions were obliged to finance trade goods in Siam before departing, and hope to recover their outlay upon return in proportion to the price realized on the sale overseas.

It was through the influence of his English friends that Phaulkon managed to acquire the necessary investment and fit out a ship for the Mission to Persia. Raising the necessary investment, however, was not the most difficult part of the operation; finding a crew willing to sail with him was Phaulkon's greater challenge. As if every ship on the Seven Seas had suddenly taken on hands at Ayutthaya, the Greek was dismayed that he could find not a single seasoned Chinese nor Indian seaman willing to be hired. He knew this was an impossible situation that could only be the work of the powerful Moors, who must have bribed or frightened away all crewmen. Not to be beaten, he scoured the docks and inns of the English Quarter until he found an old bosun he had once served under and paid him a small fortune to press sufficient drunks and cutthroats into service.

It was a fearsome crew he finally sailed with. Scarcely had his ship cleared land when a mutiny threatened. Phaulkon was in the stern with his bosun when a dozen of the crew gathered in the well of the ship and pushed forward a spokesman, who demanded that Phaulkon alter course and relinquish his command on Pain of Death. The men, however, were either landlubbers or cowardly loafers, whereas the Greek had survived twenty years at sea. He calmly asked the spokesman to step up and make his proposition.

When the man had moved within arms length of him, Phaulkon said so that all could hear, "Nay, my friend, it is mutiny that brings down the Pain of Death." With the swiftness of a striking snake, he pulled a knife from his belt and slit the man's throat in a single sweep of his arm. Before his victim had fallen to the deck, he had turned his cold black eyes onto the other would-be mutineers. They, seeing that Phaulkon, joined by the bosun and a half dozen loyal crewmen, meant to make a fight of it, lost heart and shuffled away.

With threats and the promise of a bonus on the safe return to Ayutthaya, Phaulkon succeeded in quelling his crew and, secretly, he enjoyed the constant vigilance and authority he needed to exert as it enlivened an otherwise tedious voyage, both on the journey out and the passage home. He took no pleasure in the trade, which he successfully accomplished in Persia, and felt instead only a stifling impatience.

Unlike when he was in partnership with Burnaby and White, he no longer saw trade as an end in itself, but only a means towards some Greater Goal.

Ayutthaya
30th September, 1680

I have returned from Persia. Though it was a terrible voyage, it has allowed me to achieve much. The Barcalon is delighted with me, and not a little amazed.

"Unbelievable! My dear Phaulkon," he told me after I had presented the Accounts of the Voyage. "This is double the sum the Moors have ever brought me from Persia." He gloated over the figures, supposing the profit owed to my superior trading skills. In truth, though I never mentioned it, any merchant of experience could have done the same, but it was my wisdom, some might say my folly, to have taken no gain for myself, and hence the greater return for the Barcalon. I have shown myself more clever than the Moors—and this was my first masterstroke.

My second was to follow moments later.

I was amused at His Excellency's delight in my Mission, and for a while I said nothing.

"There is one other matter I would raise, should it please you, Your Excellency," I said when I judged the moment ripe. "It relates not to my voyage but to the Moors' arrangements for hosting the last Mission from Golconda. I have been examining their invoices, which bill His Majesty for unusually high expenses. I think you will find the reckoning is out; by my account the King owes nothing, rather the Moors are indebted to the sum of 60,000 crowns. I have spoken with the claimants and after a little . . . what should I say . . . a little confusion, they came to agree that my arithmetic is correct."

I admit I had practised the speech, but it worked admirably. The Barcalon examined the papers I handed him and saw, as he could not fail to, that I was correct. Again, he was full of praise for me, and assured me he would inform King Narai of my shrewd and dedicated service.

As he seemed receptive to my arguments, I deemed it opportune to paint the blackest picture I could of the Moors. "Your Excellency," I said, "it is not just the matter of these rascals making profits at His Majesty's Expense. So powerful are they that they could, I fear, undertake all, supplant the Mandarins, and in a short time make themselves masters of the King's Storehouses and of the King himself, if he should refuse to embrace the Law of Mohammed. . . .

"Remember, Persia, Achin, Golconda are all Mohammedan Kingdoms who send Embassies to us with the aim of converting His Majesty to their Faith. Even within our own borders there are many Malays who also follow the Prophet. And all these people are clannish. And can you imagine what would happen should they forge an Unholy Alliance with the Dutch, already so powerful in our waters?"

I could see the old man shudder as he imagined being murdered in his bed by some stealthy Malay creeping into his chamber at night. "You are right!" he exclaimed. "We must make arrests, torture the leaders, make an example."

"With respect, Your Excellency," I interrupted. "A more lasting solution would be, I suggest, that King Narai secure assistance from outside . . . from, say, the English or the French. I have heard it said that His Majesty is already of such a mind."

I said no more, believing it better to allow time for my ideas to take root. Making my excuses, I left the Barcalon to ponder Siam's Fate.

Affairs of State first, profit later, I thought as I returned to my rooms, well pleased with the impression of myself I had planted in the Barcalon's mind.

More and more am I convinced that I am developing a Novel Scheme by which to play an old game. Never before in Siam have profits been eschewed for personal advancement; rather it is the former that usually purchases the latter. There is, of course, always a price to pay—that I accept. I will not, however, let myself be troubled by the bitter resentment against me that my actions must have stirred up amongst the Moors. They might forgive my out-witting them, but I have touched their purses, and that is the injury to the insult. Thus in my first political success I have made my first enemies in Siam. But unless I am much mistaken and the Barcalon fails in his promises to mention me to King Narai, I have also gone far in securing one ally—the most powerful ally I could have.

7

Phaulkon's proposal to weaken the influence of the Moors by courting the favour of a foreign state was a bold one. Never before had Siam entered into an Alliance with a European power, and for its novelty alone the path was a dangerous one. And even if it were possible, its probability was in some doubt.

It was true that King Narai had turned his thoughts to France and was planning to send an Embassy to the Court of Louis XIV, but Phaulkon's belief in the English as an alternative seemed ill-founded. A month before his return from Persia, the East India Company, having learnt that Siam would not agree to its terms of purchasing a definite quota of goods each year, informed the Barcalon that it had no alternative but to close its factory in Ayutthaya, and requested the Minister assist it in collecting outstanding debts.

What the English had failed to realize was that Siam was wary of long-term trade concessions, especially since a few years earlier she had been forced to concede a monopoly on hides to the Dutch. Siam wanted an ally, whereas the English had no interest in the country, only in its trade. France, by contrast, had missionaries in Siam and was showing itself altogether more interested in the country as a nation, not a mere trade partner over which to exert its influence.

In suggesting to the Barcalon the desirability of a European ally, Phaulkon was, as he well knew, advocating a wish already held by King Narai. It was not, however, a commonly known Royal Desire, nor likely to be a popular one. As an absolute monarch, Narai might, like King Louis XIV, whom he much admired, well claim "*L'état c'est moi*," yet his subjects could be fearful of a Royal Course that threatened to lead them into unknown waters.

If Phaulkon ever for a minute pondered the possibility that Narai's Ideas might be too radical, he never let it deviate from his plan, which he believed was logical, and it was sufficient that it should be in accordance with King Narai's Thinking. If there were to be dissent, he would rise to the challenge. His coup over the Moors fed his arrogance, and his confidence grew by the day.

Throughout the last months of 1680 and well into the new year, Phaulkon vigorously pursued his duties in the Barcalon's Office. The Minister was well pleased with his services; the Greek worked harder and was more efficient than any of the Siamese, which in itself was not particularly a recommendation, but importantly it allowed the old man to indulge his natural indolence. Others were less pleased.

φ

"Who is this man. . . ? What does he want with us. . . ? I hear nothing but complaints. The Mohammedan merchants come to me, a General, whining like infants against this Phaulkon, as if I knew or cared anything about their trade."

Phra Petracha was talking to his son, Luang Sorasak, a sullen youth who lolled back on cushions in his father's apartments. Sorasak's causal attitude belied the acute attention he paid to his father's agitated talk, for resentment against Phaulkon burned also in his heart.

"He's a damned foreigner. And foreigners are trouble," Sorasak said, looking at his father, whose Air of Command and broad shoulders told of great strength in spite of his average stature.

Phra Petracha was a soldier, and feigned contempt for Courtly Life, yet he stood high in the King's Esteem, being the son of Narai's wet nurse. He had grown up in the company of the King and, in adulthood, the two men had on several occasions fought side by side against enemies who threatened the Sovereignty of Siam. To the Courtiers he was known as a fighter of remarkable courage, a swordsman of repute, and a General of great cunning whose nerve had often won him battle honours even when faced with a superior foe.

For all his prominence and intimacy with the King, Petracha had never taken part in the Governance of the Land, and showed no inclination for Public Honours. Yet he dearly loved his country and did not suffer foreigners gladly, especially the Europeans whom he held in the greatest contempt for their ill manners and greed. And now Phaulkon had reared his head above all.

"He's made enemies of the Moors," Petracha continued in his tirade to his son. "I don't give a damn for them personally, but they've always conducted our trade; it's the way things are done, and we don't need be told otherwise, especially by a foreigner. The worst is that I'm told Phaulkon has completely won over that old fool Chao Phya Kosa, who speaks constantly to Narai about the brilliance of this Greek. Only the other day His Majesty asked me if I had met him and what was he like. I should not doubt the Wisdom of my Lord Narai, but his interest in Phaulkon and this Embassy he plans to France worries me deeply. The astrologers predict only misfortune will come from seeking alliances with foreigners."

"Father, we can do nothing about the Embassy, should His Majesty wish it, but Phaulkon is but one man and it should be easy to find ways to discredit him."

Sorasak pushed himself up from his cushions, a smile dispelling his sullen air. "It would be a pleasure to bring the man down. And if this chosen Phaulkon should stumble, Lord Narai will surely see the uselessness of seeking the assistance of foreigners. Leave it to me to find a way."

Ayutthaya
20th July, 1681

The King's Embassy to France has been gone these past six months or more, and nothing yet is heard of it. I fear it has been lost at sea, and if so, it is a setback to His Majesty's Desire to woo a European ally. Fortunately, matters move more satisfactorily here, largely thanks to my own doing. I continue to consolidate my position and my stock is rising. I have not yet been granted an Audience with King Narai, but I know the Barcalon talks much of me at the nightly meetings of the Royal Council, and he tells me His Majesty is much pleased with my efforts.

There is irony, in light of the probable loss of the Embassy to France, that my greatest success here has been with the French. M. André Boureau-Deslandes has recently settled here to establish French Trade, which until now has been neglected in favour of missionary work, in which the French Catholic Mission, established by Mgr. Pallu, the Bishop of Heliopolis, is most active. I set no great store by religion, and M. Deslandes is much more to my liking. I have developed a friendship with the man, which he reciprocates, knowing, I am sure, that I am becoming well set to greatly ease his endeavours, as very soon I see myself in command of all trade with Europeans.

I have not deserted my English benefactors, Burnaby and White, though I have had little time of late to be sociable with them, the burdens of my office growing daily.

8

Towards the end of the rainy season in the year 1681, Phaulkon appeared a changed man to many of his friends. He was still engaged all hours in the service of the Barcalon's Office, and was tireless as ever in overseeing the King's Storehouses and the trade that they served, but he had become morose and withdrawn, surprisingly so for a man known for his hospitality and his almost overpowering energy. If someone asked him if anything ailed him, Phaulkon replied that the responsibilities and cares of his work were more burdensome.

It was not the truth, as George White alone among Phaulkon's friends knew. The Greek's malady was the oldest and most common; for the first time in his life he found himself falling in love.

Some time previously, Phaulkon and White had taken a stroll through the Portuguese Quarter of Ayutthaya, one of the city's longest established foreign settlements, and so appealing to the

Europeans with its three churches and well-tended gardens. In the course of their walk they met Mr. Fanique, an old dark-skinned man who was by birth part Bengali and part Japanese, but who at some time in his life had been converted to Christianity and hence his home was in that Quarter. Through his faith, upright ways, and more than average intelligence, he had made himself useful to various English merchants, and most foreigners in Ayutthaya had some acquaintance with him.

"A good day to you, Sirs . . . Mister White, Mister Constance."

Phaulkon and White returned the greeting and the three of them fell into conversation, or rather White and Fanique talked of business while Phaulkon said scarcely a word, so taken was he by the vision of Fanique's companion, an attractive and comely girl of perhaps 16 years old.

After they had parted and gone their separate ways, Phaulkon was impatient to have White tell him whom the girl was.

"Why, that was Maria, of course. His daughter. You knew he had a daughter did you not."

"A daughter, yes, but not an angel, " Phaulkon remarked. "How did that swarthy bastard sire such a fair, clear-skinned wench?"

"Oh, they're of a good family. The mother is quite high born I believe; Portuguese by descent and claims some relationship with the first Christian martyr baptized in Japan by Saint Francis. They were forced out when the Japanese exiled all the converts. Had a tough time of it when they first came here, but old Fanique's done well for himself. A bit too strict in his Papist views for my liking, though there's nothing wrong with his head for business."

For once Phaulkon was not thinking of trade or politics, and he missed White's remarks about Fanique's business acumen and his Catholic views. Later he could not recall what they talked of for the remainder of their walk, so taken was he by the sight of that slim young girl with the lively eyes.

Ayutthaya
7th September, 1681

It has been a constant source of jokes among my friends that I have been something of a ladies' man since settling in Siam. In the pattern of other Eastern ports, merchants and sailors usually take a local girl as a wife for the duration of their stay in the East. I, however, have had little inclination for any such settled relationship, being too occupied in trying to establish myself. Instead of courting, I have satisfied my needs through passing affairs with a succession of young Siamese girls, whom I find I can charm easily, they being delighted I can speak their language fluently. Occasionally an irate father or a broken heart will disturb the calm, but these are easily pacified by gifts and money. They are the exceptions, however, and overall I find sexual relations with the Siamese are freer and more easily accepted than in Europe; often just a customary courtesy to a guest—though that does not mean expectations of rewards in return for favours are any the less.

At least that has been the case until I saw Maria. Since that walk with George and the meeting with Fanique, I have not been able to stop thinking about the old man's daughter.

For the first time in my life, I find myself drawn towards another person for no clear reason. I have had—and continue to value—my professional friendships with certain men who have helped me much in my career, and I have also had my romantic fondnesses for girls, though none of these have endured beyond the time of passion. Now, in a way that I cannot adequately describe, I am so taken by the thought of Maria that I fear I must be falling in love; an emotion that I have not been acquainted with before.

As a child, my father beat me so frequently that I could never eye him with like, let alone love, and my mother, although well meaning in her own way, was so taken up with her belief in our rank, our heritage, which she considered made us better than our neighbours on Cephalonia, as to dilute any filial love I should have felt for her.

Who is this Maria? What could she be for me? I have my work, my plans. Yet is it that my Destiny is entwined with hers? It is the only way I can explain. Is it love?

9

Phaulkon appeared in some way a different man to Burnaby, George White, and his brother Samuel, when they met for dinner one evening in September. It was not simply the robe of heavy silk which their host wore instead of his former breeches and leather jerkin that surprised the Englishmen; the man who greeted them was as different inwardly as outwardly. Here, welcoming his guests into a sumptuously furnished dining room with an expansive sweep of his arm, was a man more assured, more confident, more cultured in manner than they had known before.

"Welcome my friends. My house is yours," Phaulkon said as he guided his guests to a table laden with food and wine, indulging in the role of host and showing off the expensive pleasures of life that his house now offered. Everyone knew that he had bribed the best cook in Ayutthaya to join his household.

"So, my dear Phaulkon, you prosper I see," remarked George White in admiration as he surveyed the room where mother-of-pearl-inlaid furniture and rich fabrics filled out the candlelit space.

"I prosper you say, George. Aye, well, the Barcalon gives me much responsibility, and I am told the King is well satisfied with me, so that I begin to fathom a path forward that should prove beneficial to us all. You know as well as I the Kingdom is much troubled. I have spiked the Moors' guns for a while, but it is the Dutch who go on unchecked, and His Majesty fears their influence throughout the Eastern Seas is too great. I have hopes that the English Company will step in to provide a viable alternative, but it seems content to send us fools and incompetents like that stupidly officious assistant Samuel Potts, and let slip the initiative. How think you, George."

George White was silent for a while and took a sip of wine as if to delay what he had to say before looking directly at Phaulkon. "My friend, regrettably I've become convinced that the Company has no wish to interest itself seriously with ventures in Siam. At the same time, through the factory at Madras, it attempts to stifle the independent trade of interlopers. And so, with reluctance, I propose shortly to return to England in the certainty that more awaits me there than here."

"No, surely that cannot be true," Phaulkon exclaimed.

"Yes. My mind is made up."

"Then I'll not try to dissuade you, though I'm much saddened. That you, who have given me so much. . . . I shall miss your guidance and your kindness, Sir." Phaulkon's disappointment at what would be a personal loss to him was deep and genuine, though in truth he was not surprised at his friend's decision. English influence in Siam, never strong, was crumbling.

As if reading his thoughts, Burnaby—who had appeared subdued when he arrived—remarked, "It is worse than you think, Phaulkon. I have been recalled to Bantam, and Potts is to be put in charge of the Company. George is quitting in disgust."

Phaulkon expressed further dismay and sadness, but did not say he already knew, through his spies, of the Company's intentions. Even so, to hear in his own house his two benefactors confirm what he feared, dashed any hopes he had of salvaging English assistance for Siam. Gripped with a sudden anger, he threw his goblet at the wall. "That bloody buffoon Potts is a curse. Hounding me to settle that ridiculous debt. Spite and envy is all his small mind knows."

As quickly as his tempered flared, so it died. "Let it rest. Potts will get his desserts. More fool him if he thinks he'll get the better of me."

Phaulkon sat down, apologizing for his outburst and calling the servants to bring fresh wine. They talked no more of business affairs, and soon settled to enjoy the meal of Siamese and Chinese delicacies. Throughout dinner, the talk around the table was light and easy flowing, and the Englishmen relaxed with the wit and sparkle of Phaulkon's conversation.

"The man is amazing," thought George White, not for the first time. "Bombastic one minute, outraged man of affairs the next, and then the chameleon changes again to a charming talker. I travel to England, but I wonder where and how far this Phaulkon will go." For a moment he felt a sense of foreboding. Fearing that he might cast a sense of gloom on the evening, he turned to Phaulkon—who was laughing over some joke with Burnaby—and, assuming a wry grin asked, "And how is the sweet Maria these days?"

White could have sworn that Phaulkon blushed momentarily. Certainly the laughter died on his voice, but he quickly recovered his composure.

"Ah, yes, the sweet Maria, she is most assuredly that," Phaulkon responded. "As sweet as a mango." So you have not forgotten our meeting with her and Fanique, and I won't hide the truth from you—neither have I. In fact, I confess to a wondrous curiosity about the girl. But, Gentlemen, you embarrass me. It is very possible that it is a mere passing fancy on my part and nothing more. Come . . . more wine, and tell me of your thoughts on the Future of Siam. Where are we headed? I truly value your opinions."

Ayutthaya
20th September, 1681

Today I advanced my personal affairs in a fashion quite alien to me. But, oh, so rewarding was it.

Desirous of a meeting with Maria once again to gauge the truth of the feelings that are burning in me, I made an excuse of some trade matters to call on Fanique this morning. There were real matters I could discuss with him, ask his advice upon, but in the course of this it was my hope to catch sight again of Maria, and so test what feelings she might arouse. This ruse worked better—or maybe worse—than I had anticipated.

A servant let me into the house and asked me to wait. I heard someone enter the room behind me and, turning expecting to see the old man, my eyes fell upon Maria.

"Good day to you, Senhor Phaulkon. Pray, take a seat," she said, showing no surprise at seeing me and quietly giving her regrets that her father was unwell and unable to receive visitors.

"I suppose your business must be urgent to bring you here in person all the way from the Barcalon's Office. Is there anything I can do?" she asked.

Was this child mocking me? Could she possibly have guessed my pretext? She spoke with such assurance for one so young and was in no way daunted by the status of her caller. Her poise, coupled with my surprise at seeing her rather than her father, threw me off balance, and I stuttered in saying I was sorry to hear of her father's sickness and hoped he would soon recover.

"T'is only a fever, Senhor, and if you call again in a few days I'm sure my father will be pleased to see you," she replied. "But won't you take some refreshment before you leave."

I felt unnerved, as if I, rather than Maria, were the adolescent, and was already hurrying to take my leave when she made this invitation. She summoned the servant to bring green tea, and we sat and talked. I recovered my composure and fell into easy conversation with this strangely mature girl.

I have always had a weakness for a pretty face and shapely figure, but whereas before it was the delicate, slim-hipped bodies and care-free smiles of the Siamese girls that attracted me, Maria is winning my heart in a very different way. To be true, she has a neat figure, though she is scarcely five feet tall, and her face is even-featured. She is lighter skinned than her father, inheriting blessedly the fairness of her Japanese mother, and the paternal strain is most visible in her large, black, intelligent eyes. Most men will have marked her as merely attractive, falling short of true beauty. For me there is real beauty which stems not from the physical but from her unmistakable vitality, her vigour, and, in some strange way, her almost palpable air of piety.

We sat for some time time exchanging pleasantries before I felt it would be improper to stay any longer, though I was loath to leave. She enchants me and I know not how or why.

10

"An elephant hunt. . . ? Why should this be of interest to us? It is the King we wish to see." The Head of the Persian Embassy to Ayutthaya spoke in frustration after Phaulkon had informed him of the day's programme.

"Yes, indeed, Sir, and so you shall," Phaulkon replied patiently. "The King will himself conduct the hunt. It is a pastime to which he is much given."

With these few words and a smile, the Greek effectively shut the door on the Ambassador, leaving him no alternative but to go along with the day's entertainment. To decry the hunt would suggest disrespect to the King who, as Phaulkon said, so enjoyed the sport.

A flush of pleasure swept Phaulkon's face after the Ambassador had left the room with a scarcely veiled look of contempt. This was the first time the Greek had been given charge of overseeing the hosting of a Foreign Embassy. He himself had yet to meet King

Narai in Audience, though he knew from the Barcalon that His Majesty was beginning to think highly of him, and appreciated his work in serving the interests of the Kingdom's Foreign Dealings, and this responsibility for the Persian Embassy was proof of it.

As he had told the Persian, the King would be present at the day's excursion, although Phaulkon would not be asked to speak with him. Nor was he yet invited to the Meetings of the Ministers held each night in the Inner Palace, though he harboured hopes that in time and with good fortune he would become privy to these highest levels of Court as he made himself increasingly indispensable in handling the affairs of foreigners.

Phaulkon had already come to know that nothing was ever direct in the dealings of the Siamese, and talks and negotiations always took a roundabout course. There would be meetings with Mandarins of increasingly higher Rank; banquets, entertainments; a Royal Audience merely to express welcome; and only then, maybe, could an audience of any substance be held with the King. The degree of such audiences was indicated by the number of Mandarins in attendance; perhaps forty in the first instance, then maybe twenty at the second visitation, and if there was a third there would be only six or eight, all of them close to the Monarch.

Royal Audiences alone, however, even the most intimate of occasions, would not bear immediate result, and one's petition, proposal, trade agreement, or whatever, would not be accepted, adapted, or rejected until after much discussion behind closed doors—and gain or fail in their aims, petitioners could never know just how the decision had been made and through whose influence.

It was in the fact that the Customs of Siam were so different from elsewhere that Phaulkon saw the potential for his own advancement. Without a mediator such as himself, who knew the ways of the Court, no one, least of all a European, could possibly expect to navigate a true course.

Buoyed up by thoughts of his strengthening position, and particularly pleased that he had asserted his authority over the arrogance of the Persian Ambassador, Phaulkon joined that morning the rear of the Royal Entourage that proceeded to the elephant hunt, though in truth he had no more taste for the sport than did the Persians. To him it was a tedious affair, yet he appreciated the importance of the animals—of which some 2,000 were battle trained—and the importance, too, of the delight the King took in the kind of hunt it had been his pleasure to revive in recent years.

The spectacle took place at a huge enclosure some twenty leagues around, where two rows of fires had been lit all night and men with pikes placed every ten paces. Once His Majesty had arrived on his war elephant, along with the Persian Ambassadors— also mounted, though looking far less at ease—armed men entered the enclosure, making a great sound, and gradually the ring around the hunting ground was tightened until the wild elephants trapped in the enclosure were close enough for men to throw nets over them in which the beasts' legs became entangled. As the King gave orders from his mount, war elephants, specially trained in the hunt, moved in on their wild cousins, prodding them with their tusks and marshalling them until men on the ground could fasten ropes and so manoeuver the animals to stout posts, where they were tethered and soon became docile.

That morning some twenty of the beasts were captured, and during the course of the hunt Phaulkon noticed that the King rode up to the Ambassadors and exchanged courtesies. So perhaps the Persians would not have found their time completely wasted.

ф

As Phaulkon was returning from the hunt in the afternoon, he was accosted by a man at the entrance to the Outer Palace, and thinking he was just another petitioner, the Greek did not at first recognize him.

"Mister Phaulkon. You don't remember me. . . ? Fanique."

"Why, yes, of course, Mister Fanique. You must excuse me," Phaulkon replied. "I have just returned from the Royal Hunt and am a little exhausted.

Yes, quite. But I'll only take a moment of your time if I may. I understand that you have paid court to my daughter. In this I must ask you desist. She is no girl for you. She is a devout Catholic, which you, Sir, I believe are not. We are paupers compared to you, Mister Phaulkon, but nonetheless I cannot persuade myself to give her hand to you in marriage until the day when I behold you practicing the Catholic Faith openly and with no reservations. That is all I have to say. I bid you good day."

Phaulkon had no time to express surprise at this outburst, let alone make any kind of reply, before Fanique turned and strode off down the street. Phaulkon would have followed and caught the man up and asked him to explain himself fully if it were not for an uncontrollable anger he felt bursting in his head and making him incapable of any movement.

By the time the passion has loosened its grip, Fanique had disappeared and Phaulkon realized there was no gain in running after him. He was confused; a strange emotion for him who, whether in a violent temper, in convivial mood, or ingratiatingly fawning, always knew his mind.

Ayutthaya
17th October, 1681

Fanique has confronted me with regard to my seeing his daughter. I am affronted by the man's behaviour. And his only success is to fire my passion for Maria and strengthen my resolve to take her as my wife. As my standing with the Court increases, it is only proper that I wed and soon.

On each of the days I have called on Maria whenever my time allowed, I have made no pretext to see her father. Instead, I make my intentions plain, wooing her with all the charm I have and, like an Othello, beguiling her with tales of daring and courage. Everything I tell her is true, and she may be flattered and enchanted by my wit, though I can tell she will not lose her heart to childish dreams conjured by an admirer's spellbinding talk. I am beginning to feel frustrated, for as welcoming as she is, Maria does not yield easily.

"Dear Senhor Phaulkon," she addressed me yesterday afternoon as we took refreshment at her father's house. "Your life is indeed exciting, and you have seen and done marvellous things, but I must make plain to you that none of this matters to me."

Hearing this, I stood up to take my leave, believing that all was lost and this woman, this child, would never consent to any proposal of marriage.

"Wait, Sir, there is more I have to say," she continued. "Perhaps it is more than I ought to say, but I believe honesty should come above all. . . . You are a man of true worth and accomplishment, though the more remarkable for what lays deep within you. You are many men; a kind and considerate suitor to me; a modest and respectful prospective son-in-law to my father, a strict and unbending commander in your dealings with subordinates. You are a man for all seasons, a man who can make it blissful summer or chilling winter as he chooses fit. You ask for my hand in marriage, and to that my father will decide. For me, I will gladly be your wife. I love you with all my heart, as I think you do me. Honour and trust will support us."

I scarcely believed what I was hearing. Never have I known such a forthright woman, nor a woman whose intelligence sees me so well. No man can be more fortunate than I if Maria were to become my wife. I confess that I think her strength and understanding will aid me in fulfilling my aims. Yet judge me not mercenary, for I love her truly.

For a long time I held her hand, neither of us needing words. I sensed a remarkable strength that I could only think arises from her piety and the conviction of her Faith.

I came away from meeting Maria enamoured, convinced in my mind that we will be married. But the figure of Fanique clouded my thoughts as I walked home. I have been courteous to him on the few occasions we met after he had confronted me, and hence Maria thinks me a respectful prospective son-in-law. In truth I despise the man, and if half what I hear is true, the feeling is mutual. He makes no attempt to disguise his dislike for me, and tells others that he thinks me arrogant and high-handed in my dealings with the merchants, and that even if my prospects look favourable and the King thinks highly of me, I should come to a bad end. This he does not say to my face, nor is it his main objection to my becoming his son-in-law.

I returned again last evening to formally ask for Maria's hand.

"You are still not a Catholic," Fanique again told me bluntly. "I will only give my daughter in marriage to a man who has publicly professed the Faith."

What matter? I have altered course before, and will do so again. It may well be to my advantage in more ways than one.

In Cephalonia my mother had raised me a Catholic, and our family would attend Mass every Sunday, though I always thought this had more to do with supporting my parents' claims to Venetian ancestry than to their piety. Later, during the years of service aboard English ships, I found it expedient to hold to the Anglican beliefs of my English masters, which troubled my conscience none at all. Here, in Siam, there is again a shift in my Religious Sense—I call it no more than that, for religion I merely acknowledge—and it is mostly with Catholics, especially the French Missionaries, that I consort. Do not misunderstand, my friendships are not prompted by Religious Fervor; it is simply that I lose no occasion to broaden my knowledge, and I find the conversation of the Catholics in Ayutthaya stimulating by way of academic discussion. I feel no need nor desire to express any personal Faith.

But now with Fanique's admonition echoing in my head every time I think of Maria, I begin to view religion in a new light. One of my acquaintances is a Flemish Jesuit, Fr. Antoine Thomas, who is stopping in Ayutthaya before continuing his journey to visit Catholic Missions further east. We talk much about Articles of Faith, about the Pope, and about the differences with the English Church.

I am not so vain that I do not think that Fr. Thomas simply enjoys my conversation, lively though our discourses are, and I believe he has ulterior motives in seeking me out. The Catholic Missionaries are very active in Siam, and for them to gain a convert in someone with my influence in the Land would be a victory. Now I have my own reasons for pursuing a friendship with Fr. Thomas. I am determined to marry Maria, and if to do so I must become a Catholic, then I will, and I would rather it be through the guidance of a Jesuit—people I consider more Intellectual than the other priests of the French Catholic Mission in Ayutthaya.

In fact, the more I consider it, the more it suits me. By far the largest group of missionaries in Siam are the French, and France is the ally King Narai most seeks—an alliance that I will be better placed to negotiate if I share their Religious Convictions.

11

Late at night shortly after the New Year, Phaulkon lay stricken on his bed, twisting and turning in sweat-soaked sheets as fever gripped him. A servant sat by his bedside mopping his brow with cold water, although twice the bowl had been flung from his hands when Phaulkon became delirious and flailed wildly.

At moments when the fever left him and his mind cleared, he thought of Maria and of religion, and of his own possible death. Neither his Faith nor the fact of his mortality had much troubled him before, yet now it was the vision of Maria that inspired a desperate will to live, to marry, and, with Maria's Faith and strength, to fulfill the life he saw as his.

He sent his servant to summon Fr. Thomas who came despite the late hour, and knelt at Phaulkon's bedside.

"Father, the fever is much upon me and I fear for my life." Phaulkon spoke in a hoarse whisper.

"Rest, my son, rest," the priest said softly.

"Father, I am outside the Church, and wish you to guide me so that I might not die unrepentant."

"You must become strong," Fr. Thomas replied. "There will be time. Trust in God. When you are well, I will instruct you so that you may adjure your errors. Let us pray for God's safe keeping."

Fr. Thomas was a patient as well as a pious man, and was fervent in his prayers as he truly wished this man to recover so that a conversion would be of benefit to the Church and God. He was very conscious of Phaulkon's growing influence in the King's Foreign Affairs, and a Catholic at Court would vastly assist the Church's work in Siam. He justified his expediency to himself by believing the Greek to be a true penitent, though he could not properly adjure his sins whilst in the grip of fever.

Others too, prayed. The Moors and the English East India Company Officers in Ayutthaya beseeched their own gods that Phaulkon would die. But within the week, he recovered.

Fr. Thomas returned to visit Phaulkon as soon as news of his recovery reached him.

"My dear Phaulkon, I thank God that he has chosen to spare you. And now you must choose the True Path," he said. "But it is not right that you simply cast aside your Anglican beliefs. First, I ask you to seek a retreat, meditate on the exercises of Saint Ignatius, and in time make a General Confession. Then, your sins absolved, it would be fitting to take a Catholic wife and so make firm your conversion."

"Father, all that you say will be," Phaulkon replied. "The time is right and I see clearly my path. Indeed, too, there is one that I dearly love who will be my Catholic bride."

"The charming Maria. Yes, that I know, my son. I see her as God's Instrument to lead you to the Path of Righteousness.

φ

It was done. Phaulkon took instruction under Fr. Thomas, entered into a retreat and, on 2nd May in the Year of Our Lord 1682, he made a simple public profession of his Faith in the Church of the Portuguese Jesuits at Ayutthaya.

One week later, Phaulkon married Maria in the same church, Fanique no longer putting any obstacles in his way as the old man had witnessed Phaulkon's profession of Faith and the Communion he took shortly afterwards.

The wedding was a very solemn affair, doubtless owing to the great surprise of many at Phaulkon's recent conversion. Standing at the altar he was forced to suppress a smile when the idea entered his head that perhaps half the congregation was expecting a thunderbolt to strike him dead as a False Convert. Maria was as radiant as ever, but what pleased Phaulkon most was that the King and many of the Courtiers sent lavish gifts in celebration of their marriage. Phaulkon could not help but think that he had a Royal Blessing.

ф

Scarcely had Phaulkon's marriage been consummated than it very nearly ended; saved only by the prudence and good sense of Maria.

Before he had met Maria, Phaulkon had come to the attention of one of the Ladies of the Court, who bethought to win him to her service. Her chosen medium to accomplish this was one of her own handmaidens whom she thought most likely to turn Phaulkon's head. She sent the girl to him with the behest that he Cherish her for her Mistress' Sake, and Phaulkon was not slow to comply, and in time a child was born to them.

Before his marriage to Maria, Phaulkon renounced the girl and considered the incident finished. But the secrets of husbands are not so easily kept from wives, and Maria came to learn of the mistress and the baby daughter her husband had fathered. Far from upbraiding her husband, Maria ordered the wretched mother to give her the child so that she may bring it up as her own.

Phaulkon was greatly moved by his wife's actions, and knew he had married well. Her strength would be his strength.

Ayutthaya
13th July, 1682

Never have I been happier. My marriage to Maria has given me new life and a fresh commitment to seek my Fate and fortune in Siam. And now this day, I have been given news of the chance I have long awaited. I am finally to meet the King in Audience.

This morning the Barcalon summoned me and informed me—as I already knew—that Mgr. Pallu, the Bishop of Heliopolis, was visiting Ayutthaya for the third time, bearing a letter from Louis XIV of France for our King Narai, asking him to extend his hospitality to French traders, who are now beginning to settle in the country under the leadership of my good friend M. Boureau-Deslandes, the French Agent here.

"His Majesty wishes that you interpret for Monsignor Pallu, as he does not know Siamese and the King does not speak French," the Barcalon said. "Monsignor Pallu will speak in Portuguese, which you know rather than French, and this you will translate into the Courtly Manner. There will also be a letter from the Roman Pope, I forget his name. Do you understand. . . ?

"It is an issue of extreme important in securing our good relations with the French in accordance with His Majesty's Wishes," the Barcalon continued. "There must be no mistakes. As this will be the first time you will have been in the King's Presence, I will brief you fully on the protocol."

I could scarcely believe what I was hearing. This is the opportunity for which I have been waiting, praying, for months. And yet I am concerned lest I should fail in my service to him.

I gazed out of the window at the rain falling on the gardens and turning the palm fronds the colour of washed emeralds. I needed to mask my anxiety and allow myself time to think, well aware as I was of embarking upon a new stage in my life.

"Well?" the Barcalon snapped impatiently at me, shaking me out of my reverie. I turned and assured His Excellency that I was most honoured and would make every effort to conduct myself as he would wish.

My mind now races over the events of the past months. Everything seems to be falling into place, and I begin to discern more clearly a pattern to my life and what I might achieve. My conversion to the Catholic Faith and my marriage have led me to ponder much on the role of the French Missionaries and of France, and how religion and trade might mutually prosper, each assisting the other. With such plans gradually forming in my mind, I have recently made a point of regularly entertaining M. Boureau-Deslandes at my house in China Street. I remember how on his first visit he had admired the portrait of Louis XIV which hangs on the wall at home, and I remarked that perhaps it was not only the French who sought to bask in the Glory of the Sun King.

12

Just before the Audience with Mgr. Pallu was due to commence, dark clouds loomed over the Palace, as is the way with the monsoons, and the rain fell solid and vertical. Thus the arrival of the Courtiers and Mgr. Pallu, accompanied by the Barcalon and Phaulkon at the Audience, was conducted with more haste than decorum.

Once assembled inside the gilt and mirrored chamber, the Courtiers knelt before the interior window set high up in the centre of the far wall, its opening covered by a silk curtain. The Barcalon led the Bishop and Phaulkon to the front, and bade them kneel. There soon followed a fanfare of trumpets and the beating of drums, and the curtain parted to reveal the King.

Phaulkon was too awestruck by the occasion to appreciate much detail, and only half heard the Barcalon introducing Mgr. Pallu, and the latter reading the letters from Louis XIV and the Pope. Then

Phaulkon translated, keeping his head bowed. Almost before he realized, the Audience was over and the curtain drawn across to conceal the King.

Phaulkon was still in a daydream when the Barcalon told him the King had earlier expressed a wish that Phaulkon see him after the Audience, and while the Minister escorted Mgr. Pallu from the hall, a guard led the Greek to an ante-chamber, where Narai sat cross-legged on an elevated throne of gilded wood.

"We are much gratified, Mister Constance, is it not . . . or Phaulkon. . . ?"

"Your Majesty, I am your servant," Phaulkon replied. "Both are my names, though I am also called The Greek after the land of my birth."

"Let it be Constance. I like the sound of it." King Narai smiled upon the prostrate Phaulkon, his admiration for this curious foreigner growing to hear him speak the Language of Court.

Narai was a lively and attractive man, below average height but well set up and holding himself straight. His manner was marked with kindness and gentleness, while his great black eyes were full of intelligence. He was known to be an active man, passionately fond of the elephant hunt; yet he was adverse to war—although when compelled to take up the sword, no Eastern Monarch had a greater taste for glory.

"We are much pleased with the Audience with Monsignor Pallu," Narai said. "It is our aim to cultivate good relations with France, and the Monsignor is a link between our two nations. The success of our receiving this Audience, it is our pleasure to say, owes not a little to your most competent handling of matters. Your sharp mind and nimble wit commend themselves to us. You are clearly a man of intelligence and fine sensibility. Tell me of your history and what brings you to this Land of ours."

Not daring to look up, Phaulkon stared at a square of floor six inches from his eyes and, taking this as his audience, lost all fear and thus spoke with an ease and confidence that most found impossible to muster in the presence of the Lord of Life. He spoke of his childhood on Cephalonia, of his years with the East India Company, and of how he came to Siam and so joined the office of the Barcalon in order to offer his humble talents to the Service of His Majesty. Each word was carefully edited, though so smoothly did his speech flow that Phaulkon himself was lost in his own discourse. To the King's questions he answered with all the knowledge that a man of parts should possess, putting to excellent use all he had gleaned from the men of breeding whose company he had sought in the past. Few could have matched the sheer brilliance, indeed genius, of such easy and wide-ranging discourse from a man of so little formal learning. Even those most intimate with Phaulkon would have marvelled at his speech and the self-possession which in daily intercourse was often lost to his hot temper.

Narai was captivated from the first, delighted in this man who was neither mealy-mouthed like the Siamese Courtiers, nor boastful like the Europeans who sought his Favour.

Over the following months, King Narai summoned Phaulkon frequently to speak with him of the Court and military affairs of the European Monarchs, especially King Louis XIV of France, for whom Narai had developed a marked admiration. Sometimes he would call an Audience in the morning and another in the afternoon, each time keeping Phaulkon talking for hours at a stretch.

Ayutthaya
4th October, 1682

Royal Audiences are now an established pattern in my official life, and I feel more secure in my position, better able to deal with anyone on an equal footing. At first I was wary, in awe of His Majesty's Absolute Rule, and of the knowledge that this monarch wields the power of life and death over not only His Subjects, but also over those foreigners who seek their fortunes in His Kingdom. What is a happy whim can so easily turn to mistrust and Narai become displeased. I trust I am wise enough never to let familiarity breed contempt, and I will make certain my discourses intrigue the King while never exhausting the possibilities. The more I speak, the more Narai listens and quizzes me, and so the more my confidence grows. If His Majesty's Word is law, so should his Favour be an all-embracing Protection.

I am naturally flattered by the King's Attention; it feeds a certain vanity and brings the satisfaction that I have achieved a Status above the common man. I remember how as a child I despised my parents for harbouring pretensions above their station. Am I now similarly deluding myself? How well do we see in others what is hidden within ourselves.

But I am successful and rightly proud. It is through my own efforts that I have established myself here as a Royal Servant in Siam, and in that I do not see any of the luck by which lesser men reverse their fortunes with little struggle of their own.

For the present, I have no clear plan as to what my ultimate reward will be, and fulfilled pride is sufficient unto itself. I know I have risen higher in the Siamese world than any other foreigner ever has, and that assuages some of the gnawing, inexplicable hunger I have felt since a boy.

What I do know is that the grand style I am now able to adopt, and the authority I command—never letting an advantage slip by, never forgetting a slight against me—provoke much envy both from the Siamese Mandarins and from certain Officials of the English East India Company, to whom I am what they call an Upstart. My position would be precarious in the extreme if I had not demonstrated my genuine loyalty and true worth to my Siamese Lord. In exposing the cupidity of the Moors to the Barcalon, I seek to serve the King's Interests, as I did in interpreting for Mgr. Pallu, and so, I believe, it is now treacherous for anyone to attack me without also attacking the Work of His Majesty.

I also keep faith with my early benefactors, Richard Burnaby and George White, as well as Samuel White who, unlike his brother, is a rogue, though no less likable and useful for it. If I fail to show deference to those I think unworthy, and give no mercy in overriding those, like the Moors, whom I see working against the King's Interests, I do value my friends, continuing in trading ventures with them and keeping an open house. As for my despised enemies, nóne more so than Phra Petracha and his vicious son Sorasak—as well as the drunkard Potts, of the Company—I accept that they vilify me.

13

As the annual rains drew to a close and the people of Ayutthaya looked forward to the coming months of dry, cool weather,
Phra Petracha's hot-headed son Sorasak felt none of the relief in
the change of season. Talk among the Mandarins of Phaulkon's now
almost constant meetings with the King incensed the young
Courtier, who was outraged that the Monarch could show such
favouritism to a foreigner. As his anger mounted, he felt he must
take action before "this Greek," as he called Phaulkon, rose so high
in Narai's Estimation that he would be beyond his reach. Showing
more fire than reason, he misjudged his moment.

His plan was simple. As a Courtier with Rights of Supervision
over ordinary foreigners in the Capital, he sought to discredit
Phaulkon by arresting two of his English friends—two quite
blameless merchants—on a false charge of breeching the Royal
Monopoly on trade.

As efficient as he was ambitious, Phaulkon had documents to prove the men's innocence, and that there had been no irregularities in their trade. When he showed this evidence to the King, the latter ordered the immediate release of those whom Sorasak had arrested.

The young Courtier was furious his scheme had failed and, refusing to give up, he next attempted to make Phaulkon appear the aggressor. His idea was to insult the Greek in public, knowing that any affront to Phaulkon's pride was bound to trigger his temper.

It was a standing order that anyone entering the Palace Courtyard should leave their weapons and their attendants there before proceeding towards the Royal Apartments. On a morning in late October, Phaulkon was dutifully complying with the rule when Sorasak marched up to him, pushing himself rudely close.

"You lying Greek bastard," Sorasak yelled. "You cheating scum. You filthy foreigner who thinks he's a king's equal."

He continued to scream abuse at Phaulkon, who was unarmed, and began pushing him back against the courtyard wall.

The Greek neither answered back his tormentor, nor sought to take a stand, instead neatly sidestepping Sorasak's jabbing elbowing. Several Courtiers standing nearby saw the affray, and it was Sorasak's belief that they, seeing a common enemy, would join in and cause a brawl for which Phaulkon could be blamed as the perpetrator.

The men stood their ground, however, possibly out of fear of incurring the King's Displeasure at such unseemly conduct within the Palace Compound, or perhaps because they admired the way in which the European stood his ground and brushed aside Sorasak's taunts as if they were nothing but the flailings of an ill-tempered infant. It was clear to them that Phaulkon managed to remain in command of himself. He was playing with the youth, allowing him to rant and rage and push and shove when at any moment he could have knocked the younger man to the ground.

At last realizing no one would join him, Sorasak flung a final insult and spat at Phaulkon's feet before sweeping out of the gate with hatred in his heart.

Ayutthaya
28th October, 1682

False arrests of Englishmen, and now a personal attack by that dangerous hot-head Sorasak; indeed I must be succeeding to so infuriate this enemy that he takes such rash and foolish actions. He is little more than a boy, a mere mosquito. Yet I would be unwise to dismiss him as such; I am sure his wild actions are not his alone, and that his father, Phra Petracha, stands behind him.

Yes, Petracha. Now here is a man I must watch. He plays a cunning game, never showing his hand, always in the background, and although he professes no interest in Court Life, I fear he is like a cobra waiting to strike.

I will not, however, let my concerns about Petracha and Sorasak, nor the ravings of Potts—who is still pressing me in the Most Ungentlemanly Manner to settle a trifling debt I have with the English Company—detract me from my work and my Duty, the value of which is reflected in the increased profits of the Treasury. Putting the State above individuals does not, I know, please all, but I believe in fair dealing. There are His Majesty's Profits and private profits—both can be made if there is justice. I bow only to the King, my master—never to those whose wiles would cheat the State.

There are some, I dare say, who will think I am stepping above myself. That does not worry me—I know full well my own worth. Why only the day before yesterday, shortly after the episode with Sorasak, I was hunting wild buffalo with the King when, running ahead in my enthusiasm, I found myself caught amid a herd of the beasts and one butted me so close that my tunic was torn. Seeing my predicament, the King himself and his guard ran to my rescue. It was a humbling moment for me, at the same time ennobling as I saw the concern on Narai's Face. And that was no mere fancy; the following day I received from the King a parcel of Chinese silks and Indian fabrics, along with a large sum of money, together with a kind note from His Majesty that I should use these gifts to make good the loss of my tunic.

Should I not be well pleased? And so much the more now that my dear wife tells me today that she has been with child these past two months.

14

The cursing of Samuel Potts caught the attention of an old man passing by in the street outside. Looking in at the window, he saw an ill-kempt Englishman ranting loudly to himself.

"That jumped-up Greek bastard. That cabin boy. That powder monkey. I'll fix him once and for all. Thinks he's better than me now he's in the King's Service. Well, that's just the King of Siam, while I, Samuel Potts, English Gentleman, am in charge of the Ayutthaya offices of the East India Company, which receives its charter from the King of England."

The sight of this wild foreigner, stupid with drink and anger, made the old man chuckle to himself. It confirmed what he had long thought: that all foreigners were mad.

Unaware that he was being observed, and uncaring if he had known, Potts paced back and forth across the floor of the teakwood house adjoining the storehouses that served as home, office, and factory for the English East India Company at Ayutthaya. The ramshackle look of the buildings that spoke poorly of the state of the Company's affairs was reflected in the disheveled state of Potts himself. Striding to and fro, his shirt-tails flying loose from his breeches, he stared wildly around at the spilled inkwell, the clutter of stained and crumpled papers strewn across the desk, and debris of dirty dinner plates scattered on the floor. A layer of dust covered everything, the mustiness accentuated by motes caught in the last rays of the day's sunlight streaming though the unshuttered windows.

"God, what a mess," he thought, reaching for the brandy flask and refilling his glass. "It's all his bloody fault, that damn Greek." Thinking of what he should put in his overdue reports to his masters at Bantam and in England, he began to dictate a letter to the empty room as he paced and slurped his drink. "We will achieve nothing until this bramble be rooted out, a thorn in all our sides. . ."

The word 'bramble' caught his fancy. "Ah, that's good. . . . Sharp but without being obviously offensive," he spoke aloud to himself, forgetting in his drunkenness that he had repeatedly used the word over the past several months in his bitter complaints to his bosses in Bantam as he sought to explain his abject failure to collect Company money owing in Siam, including a debt of some 424 catis of Phaulkon's outstanding from cloth he had bought to sell in Japan. It was this that rankled most in Potts' mind and for which, as he well knew, he had the sympathy of the Company Officials who were equally resentful of a former underling who was now rising to power in a land where they had palpably failed to make their mark, or profit. This was all the more galling since, as the Company Chiefs knew but never admitted—and which Potts could not see in his blind envy—the truth was that Burnaby and White, with the assistance of Phaulkon, could have succeeded in correcting errors made years before and reversed their fortunes in Siam.

By December 1682, it was too late. Orders had gone out for Potts and his colleague Thomas Ivatt to conclude the Company affairs at Ayutthaya and close down the factory.

"Well, did you get it?" Potts looked up as Ivatt entered the room.

"Sir, Phaulkon refused to see me. He did send out a message, however, in which he again acknowledged the debt and said it would be repaid in full once the copper shipment arrives from Japan."

"Yes, yes. We've heard all that before. It's what he's been fobbing us off with for months. But where is that damn shipment? Does it exist or is it a creation of his deceitful mind? That is the question, my stupid little Thomas."

"Exactly, Sir."

Ivatt was a small man, yet with a dignified air, and he could scarcely veil his contempt for his superior—and only with difficulty did he stop himself from saying Potts was a fool to disparage Phaulkon, let alone personally antagonize him. Like it or not, everyone knew the Greek's star was rising and, while he was a hard man to deal with, he could bring himself to be fair if one but were fair with him.

Ivatt moved towards the door saying he would retire for the rest of the evening to his chamber where he had letters to write, although the truth was that he could not endure Potts' company for a minute more than necessary. Potts shrugged and reached for the flask, overfilled his glass, and slopped brandy over the papers on his desk. He stared blearily at the pool of alcohol and thought how tempting it was to put a match to all the mess. "It's a thought," he mumbled to himself. "Indeed, a thought."

Later, as he was leaving to spend the night with his mistress, Potts knocked over the brandy flask in reaching for his hat and forgot to snuff out the candle on the desk, his mind still consumed with Phaulkon and how he could get the better of him.

φ

In another part of the city, a little distance from the offices of the East India Company, M. Boureau-Deslandes sat in his house on the south side of the island composing a letter to the French East

India Company at Pondicherry. Mgr. Pallu had departed Siam after his Audience with King Narai, leaving Boureau-Deslandes to further the Interests of the French in the country. He, like Potts, was similarly thinking about Phaulkon, but in an even-tempered manner. He wrote quickly in his enthusiasm:

> *This Greek does more trade than all the other merchants put together: he has two audiences a day with the King, who being of an Inquisitive Turn of Mind, and having a liking for the fellow, detains him for two or three hours on end. You can imagine how useful the friendship of such a man must be if you realize that the only means we have of bringing our wants to the ears of the King is through the medium of someone who enjoys his confidence. I am on very friendly terms with him . . .*

Boureau-Deslandes wrote on at length, convinced in the correctness of his recommendation of Phaulkon, and that he was the key if France was to have any influence in Siam. Just before midnight he laid aside his pen and was sealing the finished letter with wax when his servant burst into the room and in a frantic voice cried out, "Master, quick, the city's on fire!"

"Slowly, man, slowly. What are you talking about?" Boureau-Deslandes was used to his servant's excitability and predilection for exaggeration. Only the previous week he had ran around the house yelling the cook was dying, though she had only sliced a finger while cutting vegetables. Unable to get any sense out of the man, Boureau-Deslandes pushed him aside, pulled open the front door, and peered out into the darkness. A slight breeze was stirring the cool night air but otherwise nothing moved in the slumbering city. He was about to shut the door and admonish his man for the unwarranted alarm when his eye was caught by a glow in the direction of the English Quarter. The sky grew brighter as he looked, filling with an angry redness that rent the surrounding darkness.

"Good Lord! That's the English Company. It's on fire." Boureau-Deslandes hurried back into the room and called for his hat and embroidered topcoat, which he flung over his shoulders as he ran out into the December night.

By the time he reached the English Compound it seemed as if half the population of Ayutthaya had left their beds to come and gloat at the disaster, just as they did when boats collided or sank on the canals and people drowned. But there were no dead or dying victims to be seen here, only Potts standing in his nightshirt looking stunned and rushing around screaming at the onlookers to do something. Without much enthusiasm, a few citizens vainly searched for jars, but they knew there was nothing to be done. The wooden buildings were tinder dry, there having been no rain for more than two months, and there was no stopping the fire from running its course. Flames quickly enveloped the buildings; beams collapsed; and soon the entire roof fell in, reducing the English headquarters to a flaming bonfire that consumed all the Company's monies, ledgers, and merchandise.

By that time Phaulkon had heard the news and had hurried to the scene. After greeting Boureau-Deslandes and learning what little the Frenchman knew of the conflagration, he went to examine the smoldering remains. He appeared calmly resigned to the calamity when Potts came rushing up to him.

Potts, his eyes bloodshot from drink or the smoke, was shaking with rage as he flung abuse and accusation into the face of Phaulkon. "You bastard. You bloody Greek bastard. You fired my offices to destroy proof of your debt to us. Well, it won't work. You'll pay for this and more."

"You'll keep a civil tongue in your head when you address me, *Mister* Potts," Phaulkon responded. "You are a fool and a drunkard. You must have set the blaze yourself when you were wild with drink. Or else deliberately to hide the evidence of your Gross Mismanagement of Company affairs. My debt will be paid forthwith. You will need the money now that you are homeless. Let that, Sir, be an end of the matter between us."

Phaulkon turned and walked away.

Ayutthaya
11th May, 1683

I have had no time for this journal for the past half year, so full have my days been. There has been great joy and sorrow—what be one without the other?—and in the fullness of things I have fared well, and will continue to do so provided certain matters can be settled to my satisfaction.

But first I record with great pride that a son has been born to me. Yes, Maria has presented us with a fine boy whom we will christen Jorge, in honour of my great benefactor George White.

During the last few weeks before the birth, Maria and I prayed fervently each night, and our prayers were answered; Maria was blessed with an easy delivery and our son is whole and healthy. He, together with my other child, João, born out of wedlock and so generously adopted by Maria, fills me with joy and my life moves closer to fulfillment.

Much strengthened in myself through the joy my family brings me, I devote myself to the Affairs of Siam with ever keener interest. Since the fire of December last, Potts, like the Company he represents, has become a spent force at Ayutthaya. The wretch barely manages to scrape by as he seeks to maintain his position, though I would soon as throw him in jail if I had but half an excuse.

Little Ivatt is a different matter. I have grown to like this worthy man, whom I have now taken into my own household since the fire made him without home or occupation. He will, I am sure, be of some use to me. So, too, could Burnaby now that I learn he has returned to Ayutthaya from Bantam and is, likewise, without employment since he quit the Company's Service.

Alas, George White's wife has died and he is returned to London, but his brother, Samuel, who has some experience of trade at Mergui—that most vital port for the Indian Trade on the Andaman Coast—could be persuaded to join me in the plan that is beginning to form in my mind and which should profit us all—Siam and our own individual trade.

It is my aim to make Siam richer and possess greater power than she has ever known before by making full use of her geographical position. If I can control the Indian Trade through Mergui, and at Ayutthaya we consolidate trade with India and Japan, my own position will be strengthened and the Royal Treasury mightily enriched. The plan is simple in that we merely seek to aggrandize the potential Siam already possesses; the difficulty is in finding the implements with which to effect my plan. Hence Messrs Burnaby, White, and Ivatt, whom I will take into Royal Service and place at Mergui, and then, as the English Company appears too weak and contrary, I shall do all in my power to further the King's Wish for an alliance with France, and then use the French to protect my position at Ayutthaya. It is not so much that I support the French and the Catholic Religion, but it is that they can support me and so enable me to bring my plans for Siam's Enrichment to fruition.

15

Towards the middle of the year 1683, Chao Phya Kosa Tibodi fell ill and died. His death was much hastened by the flogging he had received on the King's Orders in punishment for taking one bribe too many. He was afterwards repentant and saw he had deserved his punishment. Phaulkon stood by his old mentor until the last, and afterwards aided the man's family to recover from their fall from grace.

Phaulkon's assistance to the former Barcalon's family was as courageous as it was compassionate, for it could have compromised his own standing in the eyes of King Narai, who had then to choose a successor to Chao Phya Kosa Tibodi.

The King found himself much troubled in deciding who should be the next Barcalon, a man who must of necessity daily negotiate with foreigners. He at first favoured Phaulkon as he believed he possessed remarkable talents and had proved himself so wise and capable in overseeing foreign trade. But he feared that his appointment might cause jealously at Court among the other Mandarins, which would undermine the Greek's authority. Finally, he decided to offer the position to his lifelong friend and trusted General, Phra Petracha.

φ

"Your Majesty does me great honour," replied Petracha when Narai made his wishes known at a Private Audience. "I wish that I was worthy to be Barcalon, but I regret to say that I am only a poor soldier, not an administrator. I know nought of trade nor of the foreigners who conduct it." Petracha spoke softly, yet though he bowed his broad shoulders and kept his hard square face lowered, his voice belied a physical power and stern character.

"With a thousand pardons, Your Majesty, I must decline Your Generous Appointment. Even the thought is more than I deserve. It is my duty to serve and protect, and this, with Your Gracious Permission, I will always strive to do as your humble servant. Let another more suited to the task, more skilled in foreign ways, uphold Your Majesty's Royal Commerce." Petracha did not look up at his King as he spoke, his eyes remaining fixed on the floor, and none could tell the sincerity of his speech.

Narai expressed no disappointment at Petracha's disinclination to become Barcalon. He did not for a moment question his loyalty, and respected his reasons for declining the Royal Offer. Since he would not become Barcalon, Narai honoured Petracha by bestowing a more fitting military honour, that of the Command of the Royal War Elephants.

φ

When Phaulkon heard the news that Petracha had turned down the post of Barcalon he was furious, frightening Maria with one of the sudden outbursts of uncontrolled temper that she had learnt, soon after her marriage, was another, darker side of the man she had known as a courteous and attentive suitor.

"Why, surely it is good that Petracha will not be Barcalon. It's a higher position than his military rank," she reasoned.

"Fool, woman. Don't you see that damned man and his un-speakable son are as greedy and rapacious as a fox in a hen run. Both have designs for the highest power, which makes them very dangerous men to cross. But if Petracha were Barcalon and I his assistant, then I would have official relationship with the man and could watch closely his actions. As a General he's potentially an independent force that I cannot control."

Phaulkon's outburst was quickly spent, and he apologized to his wife who was his most precious ally, one in whose quiet, yet deep religious faith Phaulkon found a source of strength and equanimity to counter his own volatile nature.

"Forgive me, my love, but these are trying times and I must be careful, watch everything closely if I am to retain my post in the King's Service. Petracha worries me."

Phaulkon knew he was in a difficult position. He was sure that Narai would offer him the post of Barcalon now that Petracha had declined, but if he accepted the honour he would be burdened with so many obligations that he would not be able to operate outside the Court; could no longer go wherever he chose without hind-rance. Worse, a foreigner in such a position would surely incur the fiercest jealously of the Mandarins. Honours in Siam might open many doors, but they also shut off channels for a man of inde-pendent will. Yet if he declined Narai's Honour, he risked alienating his champion.

When on the next day Phaulkon was summoned to an Audience with Narai and the Monarch, as expected, said he wished to make him Barcalon, Phaulkon called upon all his skills of tact and diplo-macy to persuade the King that the position should rightly go to a Siamese. Astute as he was, Narai saw that Phaulkon would perhaps be of greater use to him if he permitted him a freer rein than formal office would allow.

All concerned were finally satisfied when Okya Sedet was appointed titular Barcalon, and Phaulkon made his assistant with the title of Phya Wichayen.

Sedet lacked the ambition and efficiency of his predecessor, and was content to pursue his own pleasures and leave the work to Phaulkon.

Ayutthaya
10th July, 1683

I am much relieved that the question of the new Barcalon has now been resolved. It has been a most worrying time. I could not desert the old Barcalon after his downfall. Though his greedy ways had finally been his undoing, it was he, albeit persuaded by Burnaby and White, who had saved me after my disaster in the South and provided me, perhaps unwittingly, with the opportunity to rise in the King's Favour. That hard-won Patronage could so easily have been lost by my moral support for Chao Phya Kosa Tibodi and, latterly, his family (I have heard that his brother is to be made Ambassador-in-Chief to France), yet it is not in my nature to desert those who have befriended me.

Then on his death, the question of the selection of a new Barcalon could have compromised me if Narai had been angered at my declining his offer of the position. It has all turned out for the best; so long as I carry out my work, I will be unhindered by the new

Barcalon. And besides, I have my own Royal Title, which gives legitimacy to my actions. All I worry about now is Petracha. He has refused to become Barcalon, but I fear he is not honest in disclaiming Court Ambition. I think it is a waiting game he is playing. Still, I can do nothing other than keep a close eye on whatever manoeuvering he may attempt, while I forge ahead with implementing my own plans.

I wonder, does a man ever truly control his own fate? Ambition and pride are cruel masters both.

16

Phaulkon welcomed his friend to his house shortly after Burnaby had returned to Ayutthaya. "My dear Burnaby, it is a pleasure to see you back in Siam."

"Phaulkon . . . ah, pardon, Lord Phaulkon, I must say these days. I'm happy you still have time for us poor English, with what I hear of your friendships with the French Priests, not to mention your standing at Court. The man who would be king, eh? Do not forget that Portuguese rascal de Brito and the little kingdom he created at Syriam. Very nasty end he came to, and that was only seventy years ago."

"Come, come, my friend, pray do not make a jest of me," Phaulkon replied. "De Brito succeeded only by military force. I use my wits. And besides, he tangled with the Burmans; they are far more bloodthirsty than the Siamese. But let us hear no more of this nonsense. Whichever way my future may go, you were and remain my

97

True Benefactor in Siam. I shall never forget your and George's kindness when I first arrived. I owe all to you both, and you know I'm not a man who forgets his obligations. You will always be welcome under my roof. Pray, take a glass of wine." Phaulkon smiled, delighted to see his old friend again. He reached out and offered a goblet from the tray a servant was holding, feeling happy in his possession of the wealth and prestige that permitted him to play host in a Regal Manner.

"Your very good health, Sir," said Burnaby as he drank and then looked long at the cup he held. "Gold, eh Phaulkon? And these. . . ," he remarked, looking around the opulent room, ". . . Chinese furniture of mother-of-pearl inlay, Persian tapestries, silks, jewelled candlesticks. My, you've prospered mightily. Why, it was only, what, three, four years ago you were scrambling for whatever trade you could get, and that disastrous run down South. I thought you'd do well, but this I never imagined. More than any of us have achieved. What is your secret?"

Phaulkon was embarrassed and, momentarily lost for words, he fumbled with the cord of his robe, a costume he found cooler than European dress and always wore when not on Affairs of State. He would never admit to another that even as a boy he had always believed that he was destined for greatness. He still believed so, more than ever, but it would be tempting fate to utter it aloud, even to one as understanding of Phaulkon as Burnaby.

"No secret, my friend, save I am a married man now, and a father, too," Phaulkon replied. "I have a duty to my family."

"Indeed, congratulations. When may I pay my courtesies to the fair lady and give your son my blessing."

"Soon, soon. First let us eat and drink and talk of business . . . business that I trust will interest you greatly."

"Ah, Phaulkon. Your table is as bountiful as your energy and ambition are boundless."

A hospitable man by nature, Phaulkon kept more of an open house as his power and influence grew. Always the table was laden with drink and food—Chinese and European and, famously, the little Portuguese-Japanese cakes that Maria made from a recipe handed down from her mother—and many a night forty or more would sit down to dinner: merchants and missionaries, rich men and poor, liars and honest men, with whom Phaulkon would talk until sunrise, never knowing who might be of use in the future, what scrap of information would give him advantage. Names, faces, facts, he stored away in a memory that never failed him.

Phaulkon had thought much of Burnaby the past months as he plotted his ongoing course in the service of the Barcalon, an idle man who left him to his own devices and never interfered so long as the Royal Revenues were maintained. It was a situation that suited both. Although many thought Phaulkon arrogant, he was not so conceited as not to admit the need for friends he could trust; experienced and resourceful men like Burnaby and Samuel White.

φ

"Look, Richard, there is much we can accomplish." It was the first time that Phaulkon had addressed Burnaby by his Christian name. "You know, perhaps even better than I, how important Mergui is to the King's Monopolies. The port is pivotal for the Trade with India, and revenues from the whole of Tenasserim Province are huge. It is my plan—and I am confident I now have the influence at Court to succeed—to make Samuel White, who is already experienced in the Andaman Trade and a good man for all his piratical ways, *Shahbandar* or Customs Master of Mergui; and you, Richard, as the more senior man, I wish to appoint as Governor of Mergui, in unison with White. I'll also find a post for little Thomas Ivatt. What say you?"

"My dear Phaulkon, I am of course greatly honoured, and I'm sure White will do well, albeit he's not as steady a man as his brother. But what of the Mohammedans? They have always held these posts in Tenasserim. How are we to change hereditary customs?

"That's just it, my friend; change. The Mohammedans have been for too long too powerful, and Siam has suffered for it. Why, they've milked the King's Revenues for years; the Royal Monopolies should be paying far more than they are, but the Mandarins at Court cannot or care not do anything. Such has been clear to me ever since I entered the service of the Barcalon—for which I'll always be indebted to you and George . . . and now is the time to return the favour." And, he thought to himself, the time to repay others for the slights and insults he had suffered.

"All along it has been my intention to serve the King," Phaulkon continued addressing Burnaby, "in which, if done properly, there is sufficient to fill the Royal Coffers and secure our own fortunes. To this end it is my plan to bring about a new order. From the first it has been my idea to spike the guns of the Mohammedans, in which I've already had modest success in wresting from them control of the lucrative arrangements for the frequent entertainment of foreign embassies. Now the time has come to make bolder strokes. I've virtual control of the Barcalon's Office and, more importantly, I have the trust of Narai."

Phaulkon began pacing the room, warming to his argument and no longer looking at Burnaby, who remained seated, no doubt wondering at the man before him; a man more imposing now than when they had been partners in trade just four years previously.

The Greek talked at length, explaining from all angles his plan to place his friends in control of Mergui and then to seek French protection to secure Bangkok, which was both the fortified gateway to Ayutthaya and a refuge should it be needed from the latter.

"I have spoken with His Majesty already," Phaulkon went on, "and he graciously endorses the scheme. Why, ever since the English Company failed to take advantage of the Royal Overtures, Narai has sought favour with the French as a counter to the growing power of the Dutch. It will take time, but it will happen. We have unfortunately heard nothing of the Embassy Narai sent to France, and I fear it must have been lost at sea. No matter."

Burnaby listened as Phaulkon knew he would. Perhaps he did not believe all he heard, but he could not help being persuaded by the Greek's talk.

Ayutthaya
19th September, 1683

It was reported to me today that the vessel *Mexico Merchant* anchored at Bangkok last week, bringing a William Strangh and his assistant Thomas Yale. I expect both in Ayutthaya within three days.

So it appears, contrary to my belief, that the English East India Company has not yet given up on Siam. Its masters in London must be aware that the factory is not progressing and no profits are forthcoming, but they will not know the precise reasons for it. I must presume that is why Strangh—a man of some standing within the Company I am told—and Yale have been dispatched to our shores to discover the facts.

More surprising among the news to reach me is that Strangh will be seeking to obtain a Contract for the Company to supply Siam with goods to the value of some 30,000 pounds a year. Have I misjudged the English? Are they still serious about trade with us? I can scarcely believe so, although I close no doors unnecessarily.

Damn it, though, the timing is bad. The Palace has given approval for my suggested appointments of Burnaby, White, and Ivatt, and their investiture will shortly take place in Louvo, and I must ensure that that proceeds without hindrance.

Yet the King expects me to accommodate Strangh, and, for my part, I should not let any opportunity slip—though I have little optimism.

17

The long voyage from England had done nothing to improve the natural irascibility of William Strangh. Nor, upon arrival at Ayutthaya, was he put in any better temper when, accompanied by Thomas Yale and with little Ivatt to make the introductions, he met Phaulkon at the small teakwood house provided for his accommodation.

"This place is a mere dog-hole, more like a prison than a dwelling house. What is going on here, and why are you here?" barked Strangh. He had ignored an eloquent welcome from Phaulkon and, with his hands on his hips, he stood in challenge to the Greek.

"Sir, I am Constantine Phaulkon . . ."

"Yes, yes, I know who you are. The seaman formerly employed in our ships and now a Damnable Interloper. I asked what are you doing here. Why am I not introduced to the Barcalon?"

"My title is Lord Wichayen, assistant to the Barcalon, and thus charged to attend to all matters and persons concerned in the Foreign Trade of the Kingdom," Phaulkon continued, his fists clenched behind his back as he fought down a burning anger provoked by this pompous Englishman. "I much regret that the accommodation is not to your liking. I agree it is not of the finest, but as I was informed you wished the privacy of your own quarters, instead of being my guest as was intended, this is the best we are able to provide at the moment. As you must know, your own Company's offices were unfortunately destroyed by fire late last year and not yet rebuilt."

"Hmmm. Well, we shall see. I confess I am confused as to what is going on here. I met Potts, but the drunken fool couldn't tell me anything. Seems he's lost all sense, forgotten himself as an Englishman. And you, Lord Phaulkon, if that be your title, are an enigma to me, neither fish nor fowl, a European who poses as a Minister of the Siamese Court. Be that as it may, it is the Company's desire to negotiate a valuable Trade Contract, and that I cannot discuss with a subordinate, only with the Barcalon himself."

The colour rising in his face, Phaulkon stared at Strangh and knew him for the kind of Englishman he hated most—a man of privilege who however competent would always be blinded by his in-born prejudices. When he first learnt that the English Company might still be a force in Siam, that the two might work together to mutual advantage, he was prepared to negotiate on behalf of the King, but he now realized that the arrogant, ill-mannered Strangh would never have the imagination to follow his plans.

Bringing both his fists from behind his back and slamming them on the table in front of Strangh, Phaulkon was gratified to see the man startled. "I must remind you, *Mister* Strangh," he said, "that you are a guest in this country. Whatever you might want with us, you will direct through me. Should it be in Siam's Interests, I will make a proposal to our King. You will do well to remember that."

Shocked at being spoken to in such a manner by someone he considered no more than a servant, Strangh could find no words with which to answer Phaulkon. He turned to summon a servant to throw Phaulkon out of the house before he remembered that he was not in his own home. He sunk back in a chair, while Yale and Ivatt—the former silently admiring the way the Greek refused to be cowered by Strangh—looked on as Phaulkon continued:

"Let me also say that I am amazed that the Company should feel it has some kind of Privileged Position in dealing with Siam when it patently disregards the advice of an able and experienced man like George White, and instead puts its affairs in the hands of Potts, an idiot, a man who writes to London calling me a 'Greek powder monkey' and accuses me of arson; me an Official of the Siamese Court. Diplomacy would appear not to be the Company's forte. . . .

"Now, you will excuse me. I am expected at the Palace. His Majesty always summons his Ministers at this hour. We will talk again another day. . . . Oh, and I might add, should you obtain an audience with the Barcalon, he does not speak English—I always translate for him."

Ayutthaya
28th September, 1683

Just as he wished, Strangh had his interview with the Barcalon yesterday, and much to his chagrin I remained throughout. He was well received and the Barcalon asked after Strangh's health, his family back in England, and how he liked Siam.

The Englishman found it difficult to put forward his proposal for a Trade Contract, and when he did finally manage to convey the Company's proposal, the Barcalon smiled politely and, after speaking generally about the prevailing state of Siam's Commerce, signaled an end to the interview.

On our way out, Strangh glared bitterly at me, realizing he had gained nothing.

18

For two months Strangh pursued every strategy he could think of to achieve some form of arrangement between the Company and the Siamese. He refused, however, the one means that could have brought him success: Phaulkon.

There were occasions when he could have reached an agreement with the Greek, but every time they came close to meeting on even ground, Strangh's prejudiced and inflexible ways threw up insurmountable barriers. Once, he had the audacity to write to Phaulkon that he should remember that he was a former servant of the English Company and therefore in its debt, and implored him not to let self-interest sway him in allowing Interlopers, who to Strangh's mind were enemies of the Company, into the Siamese Trade.

Phaulkon answered in person, calling at Strangh's house, courteously paying his respects before speaking his business.

"With reference to your letter, Mister Strangh," he spoke calmly, "let me assure you that I will never forget that I was once a servant of the East India Company. You will do well to remember, however, that I am no longer its servant, and if I do still serve, it is to the King of Siam. As for free traders—or Interlopers as you prefer to call them—I fail to see how the Company can call for a Monopoly of English Trade in Siam when it has for some time contemplated closing down its factory here. Moreover, let me say that the monies Interlopers pay is infinitely preferable to the Siamese than the loans the Company has contracted with us in the past. A man of your experience cannot fail to see which is the better business. No, Sir, Interlopers will never be barred from our waters, no matter what contract the Company may offer.

Strangh could find no reply, and Phaulkon bade him good day without further troubling him, although not without a parting shot:

"I may add, Sir, in considering your future strategy, you might care to reflect on the difference between the English way and that of the French and the Dutch. Both the King of France and the Prince of Orange have had the courtesy to write letters to our King Narai, but from the King of England, nothing."

Strangh's jaw dropped on hearing mention of his country's two most bitter rivals, but he knew Phaulkon was correct.

As Phaulkon walked away from the house, a smile on his face, he admitted to himself that he was impressed by Strangh in one respect: he was persistent. He knew before visiting him that the man had yet again sought an interview with the Barcalon. It worried the Greek none as he knew the Barcalon would merely repeat what he had already explained regarding Siam's Policy towards to Interlopers.

ϕ

During these weeks, Strangh and Phaulkon were like swords-men, eying each other warily as they went about their respective business. The Englishman proved to be the lesser swordsman, finding his thrusts parried with ease, and his frustration so mounted daily that he often threatened to leave Siam, only to let his dogged determination make him try once more to secure agreement for the Company.

Thomas Yale urged Strangh to flatter Phaulkon, arguing this was the surest way of getting his assistance, yet so little did Strangh think of Phaulkon, and so little did he appreciate the standing the Greek had achieved in Siam, and so great were his prejudices that any flattery would have brought on apoplexy should he have managed to get the words past his lips.

Louvo
28th November, 1683

Louvo is a charming little town, no more than half a league round, that stands on the banks of a river of the same name, a day's journey north of Ayutthaya. King Narai is much pleased by the place, and chooses to spend most of his days there between November and April, indulging his favourite sport of elephant hunting; not killing the beasts but capturing them for the Royal Stables, always hoping to find a white specimen, an albino to join the one he already has—a revered animal that would presage well for the success of his reign.

The Summer Palace faces the river and is surrounded by massive crenellated walls, the merlons in the shape of lotus buds, which are pierced at regular intervals by huge gates built extraordinarily high to accommodate the Passage of His Majesty and his elephant-mounted entourage.

It was through one of these gates that this morning I entered the Palace in the Company of the King. Both of us were flushed with the thrill of the chase, our having been out early on the hunt. There then occurred an incident that caused me much consternation.

"Tomorrow we will catch that crafty old bull. We almost had him today," Narai called to me.

"Alas, Your Majesty," I replied, "I fear there can be no hunt tomorrow. It is the investiture of the Englishmen we've appointed to Mergui. A Royal Audience is expected."

"Ah, yes, those Englishmen; appointees of yours, are they not."

"You are, of course, correct, Your Majesty," I replied. We had dismounted from our elephants and were standing amid a group of Courtiers who were assisting the King, and I was uneasy that the matter of my appointees should be aired almost in public.

I noticed one of the elder Mandarins look up and then bow his head to address Narai:

"I am an old man and perhaps do not understand today's ways," the man said, "but if I may speak frankly, Your Majesty—and perhaps my years will excuse the audacity—not all the Mandarins are sure these foreigners will bring good to Siam. Phra Petracha, in particular, speaks boldly of a Foreign Plot."

I fear I was visibly shaken at these words and reached for a towel a servant was holding to wipe the dust from my face. My expression so masked, I held my breath as the King replied. I need not have feared; his trust in me was complete:

"Dear Petracha," spoke Narai. "A Trusted General, but we think he sees too well the enemy and never the ally. We are pleased with the plans of our Phaulkon here. He has all our best interests at heart. Tell the Mandarins I see nothing to concern us unduly; our Trade has to be Protected and Expanded. These men have the experience to achieve that for us."

Thankfully no more was said on the subject, and I dearly hope all will go well on the morrow.

19

Seeming like an immortal with the clear morning sunlight catching the gold thread in his elaborate Court Robes, Phaulkon led Burnaby, White, and little Thomas Ivatt into the Summer Palace at Louvo. Ivatt was of the party as the Greek had arranged that he should be appointed Agent for the Royal Monopoly at the Coromandel port of Masulipatam, which traded directly with Mergui, where Burnaby and White were to be Governor and Customs Master respectively.

Passing through the first of the Palace's three courtyards, Burnaby was so charmed by the display of flowers, palms, and fountains that he remarked the place possessed "An indescribable air of freshness and simplicity."

In the second enclosure, its white walls embedded with pieces of Chinese porcelain, the four were greeted by an Assembly of Ministers and Court Mandarins, and Phaulkon indicated to his companions that they should kneel on the carpets spread out on the ground, and bow their heads before the high window set in the building flanking the courtyard.

Presently, piercing trumpets sounded and King Narai appeared at the window and the solemn ceremony of the investiture took place—with Burnaby, White, and Ivatt presented with brocaded robes and conical hats that denoted their new ranks as Officials of Siam.

"Are we expected to wear this fancy dress?" White whispered to Phaulkon, his bowed head concealing the comment.

"Quiet! You are now in the Service of Siam. Remember that," Phaulkon reprimanded.

Ayutthaya
8th January, 1684

Strangh sailed today from Siam. He was his own undoing.
Persistent to the end, his final mistake was to try to raise a loan of
400 chests of copper. He had approached a Chinese merchant, but
the latter had been warned the Treasury might want his copper and
any loan to Strangh would therefore be illegal. The Englishman
then entertained a wild idea to appeal to the King himself, and
rushed to Louvo, where he claimed he just missed His Majesty,
though I believe he lost his nerve at the last minute. He then unwittingly played into my hands by writing a Petition to the Barcalon
who, in the usual manner, passed it on to me.

As soon as I saw the paper that Strangh had written, I knew I
was victorious in our contest of wits, but I forwent any display of
triumph. Rather than summon him to me and so rub his nose in
his failure, I called on him and addressed him in a stern but calm
fashion:

"Sir, your Petition, to which the Barcalon has asked me to reply, is quite out of order. I have to remind you that your permit allows the export of copper only, not its purchase, and any attempt to trade otherwise will incur heavy penalties. Regrettably, it appears you have no means of establishing greater trade between the Company and Siam, and accordingly should you wish to leave the country no attempt will be made to detain you."

Strangh knew when he was defeated and kept his dignity, replying only that he would make arrangements for his departure immediately. That he did, although it was not in his character to leave without a last word, and I was not surprised to receive a vicious letter from him, giving full vent to all his prejudices.

Prudent in everything he did, Strangh waited until his ship was due to clear the bar at Bangkok before dispatching the letter. On receipt of this, my first reaction was to burn it, but so scurrilous a document it is—I can almost smell the venom of Strangh's pen as he makes a litany of my "pranks" and "tricks"—that I record its essence here:

To Mr. Constant Phaulkon,

I have two of your scurrilous and false imputations of the 16 and 24 Decr to answer, with a little larger explanation of the brief though ample import of my just and parenetic charge to you of the 23 Decr, such as may suit your impolite weak capacity, which has been jumbled through your sudden and surprising elevation to a soaring Lordship and a heathenish Grace. You have lost your head as a prince of a heathen realm and believe you can speak to Englishmen as if they were crawling blacks while, you if you please, are a Greek risen from the gutter only to sink to the lowest subterfuges.

The firing of this Factory was not done without some cursed treachery (which Heaven detect!) and though I cannot charge you with it as a matter of fact, yet I cannot excuse your indirect clandestine practices, in setting so many cunning and crafty engines, and corrupting and treacherously seducing little Ivatt—a Lord forsooth!—to your practices and faction. . .

I have done with Siam, yet I hope the Honourable Company has not. . . . Therefore in the Name and on behalf of the Honourable Company I do by these presents solemnly and in Optima forma PROTEST against you Constant Phaulkon, to be liable to answer and make satisfaction in either body or estate for all the above-mentioned damages and great losses. . . .

Hurtful though this animosity is to me, I do admit that Strangh, honest, outspoken and dependable, is one of the most worthy officials of the East India Company to set foot in Siam. Yet he is the wrong choice. A true English Gentleman, he is unshakable in his sense of superiority and finds himself incapable of masking his dislike and distrust of me.

Had he not seen me as an enemy and a supporter of interlopers, and if our temperaments had been different, the English could have become the Favoured Allies of Siam; I know them better than any other nationality, their ways and their language, but I know, too, how Strangh and others like him think little of me, a lowly Greek. They thus drive me towards the French, whom I understand and like less well, but greater is my faith in them.

20

In dealing with Strangh, Phaulkon had burnt his boats as far as the English were concerned. No longer would he even harbour thoughts of the Company as an Ally of Siam.

Shortly after Strangh's departure, Phaulkon arrested two English traders, a certain Peter Crouch and his purser, because they refused to break their cargo for some bags of nails Phaulkon had requested. He had them jailed for several days without food, and although they were later released, the story of their treatment was to rankle the English for long afterwards.

Ayutthaya
25th January, 1684

Affairs move briskly here, and today—less then three weeks since Strangh's departure—a Siamese Mission has sailed for France via England. Once it was confirmed that his first Embassy, dispatched in 1680, had been lost at sea, King Narai has shown himself even more determined to continue in his overtures to the French, though this Mission bears no letter to King Louis XIV, rather it is directed to M. Colbert, the Foreign Minister, and seeks his advice on how greater bonds of friendship may be forged between France and Siam.

I do not claim credit for initiating negotiations with the French. They are not my first choice of ally, but we cannot always choose our friends. I do not enjoy great amity with the French at Ayutthaya, M. Boureau-Deslandes of the French Company was an exception, and now he has been replaced, his successor being to my mind a crook. Yet while Deslandes was in Siam we had been on cordial terms and, unlike that fool Potts, he saw the value of my friendship, realizing that the only means of influencing the King of Siam was through the medium of someone who enjoys his confidence.

Without Deslandes, the most influential Frenchmen remaining are the missionaries who, because I have been converted to the Faith by a Jesuit, do not care much for me.

Our new Mission is led by two Envoys, Khun Pichai Walit and Khun Pichit Maitri, who have been sent in the company of the missionary Fr. Bénigne Vachet. As their ship is to dock at England, from where they will proceed to Paris, I have taken the opportunity to load two cannons, as it were: I have asked Fr. Vachet to plead our case in Paris, and I am sending my own Emissary, Fr. Pascot, a discontented missionary priest now returning to Europe, whom I have charged with bringing valuable gifts to George White with the intention that my old mentor should distribute these in the right quarters to defuse any prejudice Strangh, Crouch, and others might have stirred up. The latter is an insurance to keep the English as potentially the Favoured Ally if it all possible, or at least avert reprisals against me by the Company.

I have greater hopes, however, for Vachet in France, since I have been informed that Jesuit influence is in the ascendancy at the French Court. Louis XIV's mistress, Mme. de Maintenon, is a recent convert and ardent supporter, said to control Louis' conscience and the direction of his Oriental Interests.

The strength of my own position now rests on being King Narai's Chief Confidant, a role that owes as much to my assistance in pursuing the Monarch's Cherished Wish to forge alliances as to my ingratiating personality. Yet I am ever aware that my status is precarious, depending as it does on the King's whim and his continuing good health, and I am therefore anxious for French support that will bolster his position and hence my own.

Meanwhile, Samuel White and Burnaby have taken up their posts in Mergui. And so the first part of my dual plan begins to fall into place. These Englishmen in the Service of Siam will secure our Trade in the Andaman Sea; then, if Vachet succeeds in France, I will receive French support, with which I intend to secure Bangkok, to prevent any Dutch or other unwanted intrusion, though it will also serve me against any opposition among the Mandarins here that I might encounter. Thus will I make the Siam of King Narai the most powerful nation in the East.

21

Mergui, a town of thatch and bamboo houses, lay between a low ridge hung with dense greenery and a harbour where high tide lapped at the piles of the foremost homes, the water falling back at the ebb to reveal an expanse of mud and mangroves. Stairways with undulating *naga* balustrades rose up from the winding streets to tottering teakwood monasteries that looked out over the houses and beyond the harbour to where offshore islands shimmered in the sun.

In a colourful and animated scene, brightly dressed Siamese and Burmese women haggled with Chinese merchants in the bazaars that spilled onto the streets. Mixed in with the throng were darker-skinned Malays and Indians, while the pale, hard-faced Europeans appeared outlandish. The many nations that congregated here distinguished Mergui from other towns along the Andaman Coast.

The port belonged to Siam. Siamese was the official language, even though the tongues of Pegu and Ava were more often heard in the streets, but it was the Mohammedan Indians and the Christian Europeans who controlled the trade with the ports of India across the Bay of Bengal. That trade, along with Mergui's strategic position as a gateway on the western route to Ayutthaya, gave the town its importance.

Here in Mergui, while Phaulkon awaited news from France, Samuel White's enterprise, energy, and cunning almost rivalled that of the Greek as he moved quickly to establish his position as *Shahbandar*. He first wrote to the English East India Company in Madras, humbly tendering his best services in any way that may be useful. True to the letter, he shortly afterwards assisted the Company ship *Golden Fleece*, which had sprung a leak in the Bay of Bengal. On being told of this, Phaulkon was particularly gratified, as he believed that the re-fitting and return of the vessel, together with her cargo valued at 190,000 pounds, would show the English that neither he nor Siam had any specific aims against the Company in spite of the Greek's stern treatment of Strangh.

White's next action was to fit out an old sloop, the *Prosperous*, as a man-of-war under the command of a certain Captain Coates. This also received the approval of Phaulkon who, following a proposal by White, had obtained sanction from Narai to seize merchant ships belonging to the Indian State of Golconda, where Ali Beague, Governor of its chief port of Masulipatam, had in the past caused Siam considerable losses through his corrupt practices.

Phaulkon was, however, specific in his instructions to White that the *Prosperous* should be used to take prizes from Golconda only if compensations were not made. He further ordered White to avoid any possible confrontation with the English Company's ships sailing out of Madras. No English warships were then in the Bay of Bengal, but England would be certain to dispatch them if their trade was threatened, and until Phaulkon received support from the French, he had no hope of defending Siam against another European force.

It was crucial that no one be alarmed while the Greek was still consolidating his plans.

Louvo
14th January, 1685

Almost to the year since the Siamese Mission sailed, I have received news from Europe. The voluble Vachet, I fear, must have bored the Courts of England and France with his incessant babble, but he has wit and is effective in his own way. King Charles II of England granted him an Audience, though the Monarch was under the impression he had come from China, and Vachet was shrewd enough not to correct him. So gallant was he that when the Duchess of Portsmouth asked why the Chinese suffered persecution rather than wear a pigtail as the Manchu's demanded, he replied, "Why, Your Grace, the Chinese are no less careful of their appearance than the Ladies of Europe."

Across the Channel, Vachet found the French were better informed and showed greater interest in Siam and things Siamese. He writes: "Crowds lined the streets, and shouts were heard, 'Here come the Envoys from Siam.' People left their shops and houses; those who missed seeing us in their own district ran ahead in order to catch a glimpse of us in the next one along the route. Some were polite, others mocked; but they all jostled each other to within an ace of being crushed under the horses' hoofs and by the wheels of the carriages."

More importantly, he tells me that the Siamese Embassy has been successful in its mission, and France has agreed that a Grand Embassy should be sent to Siam. Though I fancy this owes more to Vachet and France's own receptiveness than to our two Envoys Pichai and Pichit. They won no hearts and made themselves conspicuous for their boorish behaviour, complaining that the food gave them stomach pains; falling asleep during a gala performance of the opera at Versailles; refusing to kneel in church; and neglecting to take the tours designed for their edification.

Vachet was much more effective, and in his ceaseless chatter let fall how the missionaries cherished hopes of converting King Narai to Catholicism, though he omitted to say this was some time ago, and that those in Siam now view such hopes as wildly optimistic. Possibly he does not know his mistake since he has spent more time in Annam than Siam, or he may have supposed Louis XIV's influence boundless, or that France has nothing to lose. Or he may have thought not at all, carried away simply by the power and prestige of those willing to give him an audience.

Whatever passed through his mind, the effect of his rambling talks at Louis XIV's supper table has been that the French Monarch, on the recommendation of his confessor Père de la Chaise, agrees that an Embassy be sent to Siam with its objective of inviting King Narai to embrace the Catholic Faith.

That, of course, is a ridiculous goal, but I am hoping that this French Embassy will open the way for Christian Agents to be stationed in the country and so foster a better climate for French traders.

The decision of the French was not made merely on vague hopes inspired by Vachet. The more practical among his listeners were impressed by his accounts of me and how I, through my standing at the Siamese Court and my devotion to the Jesuits, will be able to reconcile what differences there may be between the wishes of the Siamese Monarch and those of the Most Christian King of France. Vachet must also have amused the French by telling them of my triumph over Strangh and the English East India Company.

It is thus that the planets are set for my star to rise, soaring in a firmament lit by the rays of the Sun King and his Glorious Embassy to Siam.

22

Bearing a letter from Louis XIV to King Narai, the French Embassy to Siam sailed under favourable winds from Brest on 3rd March, 1685 aboard the vessels *L'Oiseau*, a battleship of 45 guns, and *La Maligne*, a frigate of 24 guns.

Chosen as the French Ambassador to Siam was Chevalier Alexandre de Chaumont, a recent convert from the Huguenots and as zealous in his new Faith as in his service to King Louis. Senior among his Gentlemanly Assistants was Abbé de Choisy, an extraordinary man, brought up by his mother as a girl, and in his youth one of the most beautiful courtesans at Versailles, but now as devoted to the Church as he was formerly to the bedroom and the gambling den.

Two others of the party were to prove notable, one as friend the other as foe: Fr. Tachard, a learned Jesuit, and Claude de Forbin, de Chaumont's aide-de-camp.

Louvo
10th March, 1685

King Narai is greatly pleased with Vachet's success in France, and heartened by the news that Louis XIV will send the Grandest of Embassies to Siam. In recognition of my services, he has appointed me as one of the Kingdom's Highest-Ranking Ministers. That is gratifying, yet what serves my interests more is that Narai has chosen me to join the Secret Council. There are only five of us so trusted, the other four being His Majesty's long-serving tutor, a man of eighty years and deaf, but still sound of mind; the Grand Chamberlain; the Criminal Judge; and Phra Phi, a young man beloved by Narai and taken as his adopted son. We meet in a closed chamber of the Inner Palace every night at 10:00 to advise on the Most Vital and Sensitive Issues of State.

As befitting the Honours that have been bestowed upon me, and so that all shall see the Dignity of my Position, the King has ordered a house of brick to be built for me here in Louvo. This palatial residence will also have its own chapel and guests quarters so I might host in appropriate style the French Ambassadors we expect.

My Destiny unfolds and I cannot express the fulfillment I feel.

23

Phaulkon walked swiftly back to his chambers from an Audience with Narai and dismissed at the door the entourage of Siamese servants and Portuguese mercenaries that he thought suitable to his Rank. On entering his private rooms at the Barcalon's Office he was surprised to see a young man lounging on a sofa.

The intruder looked up, and in his insolent stare Phaulkon immediately recognized Luang Sorasak, the man he hated most in Siam, the man who, together with his father Phra Petracha, he feared most.

"You!" exclaimed Phaulkon, disturbed at the sight of this youth who, on more than one occasion in the past, had tried to discredit him and, according to the Greek's informants, had again been trying to stir up trouble.

Just the previous afternoon, Phaulkon's spies had told him, Sorasak had been drinking with his friends—equally spoilt sons of noble birth—and gave an impassioned speech in which he warned that Phaulkon sought to usurp both the King and the Lord Buddha, and have the Siamese kowtow to the Christian God. As proof of treachery, he pointed out to his fawning audience how the Greek had recently ordered a number of monks to leave their monasteries and enroll as Court Servants.

Although well aware of the danger Sorasak posed, Phaulkon had not expected the youth to confront him in person, and was thus not alarmed. Instead his mind raced to fathom what trickery Sorasak hoped to achieve by this confrontation.

"What is this intrusion?" Phaulkon demanded as he pushed the door shut behind him and stepped into the centre of the room.

Without answering, Sorasak lifted himself slowly from the sofa, moved in front of Phaulkon, and laughed in his face, his eyes cold and filled with hatred. As the sound still echoed in the room, he butted the Greek, breaking his nose. Stepping back a pace, he kicked at Phaulkon's groin, and followed with repeated punches to face and body.

The attack was so sudden and so violent that Phaulkon had no time to defend himself, and fell to floor, where he lay retching and bleeding from the nose and mouth as Sorasak kicked him into unconsciousness. Stepping over the prone man, the youth left the room in which he had spoken not a word.

Phaulkon recovered to find his servants crowding around in confusion, shaking him painfully to see if he were still alive, until one of them lifted him onto a chair. Eventually he managed to sit upright and stared hard at those around him as he gulped in lungfuls of air. No one said anything, and Phaulkon was struck dumb with anger and shame at being so humiliated; his embarrassment only relieved when a servant bought a bowl of water and a towel.

He dismissed them all from the room. The effort of washing away the blood helped him compose himself, and as soon as he felt strong enough to stand, he left immediately to seek an Audience with Narai, not that he had any desire to make a formal complaint, but an assault on one of His Majesty's Most Senior Ministers could not be concealed, and he wished to present his own Account of the matter before anyone intervened.

φ

Narai received Phaulkon without formality, dismayed at the sight of his favourite injured and bloodied.

"Our dear Constantine. Who has dared do this?" Narai asked as he held out a hand, kindly gesturing Phaulkon to rise from his knees and be seated.

Dazed as he was, Phaulkon realized this almost unprecedented break with protocol was an indication of the Esteem in which Narai held him and the extraordinary reason for the Audience. He spoke calmly and explained the full nature of Sorasak's attack.

Narai listened closely to Phaulkon's story and thought carefully before he replied. "We will order the immediate arrest of Sorasak," he said. "We cannot exonerate him, but Constantine, we understand his anger at your ordering novices out of the monkhood. In this respect you have behaved improperly."

This gentle rebuke wounded the Greek's pride just as surely as Sorasak's blows had hurt his body, and he was not greatly soothed when Narai said he would need to devise a way for showing the Mandarins why he valued his services and respected his ability and intelligence, in the hope that it would undo any animosity some Courtiers might feel towards him.

For the first time since he had entered Royal Service, Phaulkon doubted Narai, and wondered how he could so fail to understand that no rational argument could dispel the jealousy and resentment of the Mandarins. He could not relate this, and after expressing all courtesies, he left the Palace to return home and tend to his wounds.

Later, Maria, with the silent understanding she always showed, sat with her husband, her hand resting on his arm. Phaulkon's whole body was shaking with anger, and for a long time he did not speak, so choked was he by thoughts of revenge.

Maria did not pester him with questions. She needed no telling; details did not matter. She quietly prayed.

φ

Five days after Sorasak assaulted Phaulkon, he returned to Louvo—without remorse for what he had done, but fearful of Narai's Wrath. He had fled and sought refuge with his grandmother in Ayutthaya, a pious lady who had been Narai's wet nurse. In spite of her age, she made the journey to Louvo to bring back Sorasak and to intercede for him in seeking a Pardon from the King.

Unable to refuse his foster-mother, Narai granted the pardon but commanded Sorasak receive ten strokes of the cane.

Louvo
4th April, 1685

Sorasak has been punished for his attack on me, yet the hatred that inspired him appears more greatly held than I had thought. Many of the Mandarins are jealous of my Rank, considering that there are many worthy Siamese capable of undertaking my duties. That may well be so, but was it not the Wish of King Narai. What I do contend most ardently is the claim of some Courtiers that, as I am a foreigner, I cannot be loyal to the King, and may even be plotting against him. This truly offends My Honour.

Unshaken by what he sees as mere resentment, and confident in his convictions, Narai is unswayed and continues to place His Trust in me. Regrettably, however, he thought it necessary to offer proof to his Courtiers of my intelligence and value, and so devised what I considered a most childish test. Not only naïve, the trial that he arranged yesterday caused the Mandarins to lose face, and for that they will never forgive me. And yet I had no choice but to submit to the King's whim.

The Senior Mandarins, Poets, and Astrologers, together with myself, were summoned to the inner courtyard of the Palace where there stood a large cannon. Narai first called on the Courtiers and asked them to tell him how much the gun weighed. There was much shaking of heads and chatter as these worthy men walked all round the cannon pondering a solution to His Majesty's Question. After some minutes they reported that the piece was too large and too heavy for its weight to be ascertained.

"What do you think, Lord Phaulkon," he asked me.

"May I have the gun removed to the side of the canal?" I asked.

"Certainly, if that will help you," Narai replied.

Once the piece had been moved outside the Palace to the water's edge, I had it hoisted into a boat and then measured the waterline on the boat's side. The Mandarins by now were chuckling to themselves, wondering whether it was madness or trickery that I, a foreigner, was indulging in. I paid no heed and instead ordered the cannon be removed and called for sacks of rice of known weight and had them loaded onto the boat until the latter sunk to the same waterline as it had with the cannon aboard. The number of rice bags then equalled the cannon's weight, and so I gave the King his answer and he smiled in great delight.

It was schoolboy cleverness, and I will need to be a lot more devious in future to get the measure of the Mandarins, embarrassed at their failure and my success.

24

On 23rd September, 1685 the two ships bearing the French Embassy, their passengers and men in good health, dropped anchor at the bar of the Maenam River, a few leagues below Bangkok.

De Chaumont had spent almost the entire voyage deep in religious contemplation. He was an impatient and obstinate Zealot, and as soon as his ship had moored he was eager to execute his mission. He immediately sent Fr. Vachet ashore with a letter inviting the Bishop of Metellopolis, Vicar-Apostolic in Siam, to join him onboard to give account of conditions in Siam and appraise the likely reactions to his Embassy.

It took only a few minutes conversation with the Bishop for de Chaumont to realize that Siamese Protocol would not be as plain sailing as the passage from Europe.

"Convert Narai, Your Excellency? questioned the Bishop, a tall, elegant man looking aged beyond his 48 years. With respect, Sir, I am astounded that France takes for granted the King's conversion from Buddhism, a highly delicate matter and one fraught with all manner of obstacles and dangers. True, His Majesty welcomes our religion, has a liking for our missionaries, and allows us to build churches, but he is still far from being baptized. There are many steps to be taken yet."

"So, it appears that I'll be returning with you after all, my dear Chevalier." Abbé de Choisy, who could find amusement in most things, chuckled as he lolled back against the cabin's cushions. It had been the intention of the Embassy that de Choisy would remain in Siam after its work had been completed in order to effect Narai's conversion. According to the Bishop, this was unlikely to be any time soon.

De Chaumont shuddered inwardly as he listen to the Bishop, but other than a discontented look in his eyes, he managed to hide his emotions. He had little time for de Choisy's jesting nor, it seemed, for the Bishop's advice. The cabin was silent except for the slapping of the water against the ship as the Ambassador produced the text of the address he proposed to deliver to King Narai and held it out to the Bishop, asking him to peruse it.

Reading the lines of neat script, the good Bishop was again astonished. What de Chaumont had written sounded to him more like a sermon than a courteous speech to a Foreign Monarch. There were no proper salutations, and the Christian Religion was mentioned to the exclusion of all else.

The Bishop paused before making his reply: "Hmm. You must appreciate, Your Excellency, how easily the Siamese can take offence and become antagonized. Our Holy Enterprise is a most delicate matter, and if we are to achieve our goal, we must proceed cautiously. It will take time, and so I would humbly suggest this address be modified and be made less direct. With the Siamese, serious matters are best raised in an oblique fashion."

"Perhaps the Bishop of Metellopolis is fearful and prepared to bow before the heathen, but I have been charged by King Louis to effect the conversion of Narai, and I intend to carry out my task."

"You misjudge me, Sir. It is not fear that makes me cautious but a desire for the very same success you seek. But we will not succeed alone. You will have heard of a Monsieur Constantine Phaulkon, who is employed in the service of the Barcalon, although he enjoys greater power than his office would indicate, he being a Personal Favourite of King Narai. He, I would humbly suggest, could assist us greatly in our mission as an ally who has the King's ear. And remember, it is Phaulkon who will interpret for Your Excellency at the Audience with the King. Let me emphasize that, although of lowly birth, this Greek is a most intelligent and competent man, and while some find him difficult, his weakness is that of vanity, and if we were to bestow some honour upon him . . . say the Order of Saint Michel . . . he would, I believe, champion our cause."

De Chaumont listened in silence. He did not like to take advice, but he admitted to himself that the Bishop was right. To secure an ally at Court would be prudent.

ф

Feted lavishly in Bangkok by the Mandarins King Narai sent to welcome the Frenchmen, de Chaumont soon became restless at the inevitable delay, which all new arrivals in Siam endured as they awaited permission to continue upriver to Ayutthaya. Finally, on 9th October, 1685, all was ready.

The rain that had fallen the night before—the last showers of the monsoon lingering still—had cleared the air, and de Chaumont awoke to a bright fresh morning, the deep blue of the sky reflected in the still water of the river. A Royal Barge, its gilded prow carved in the form of some fabulous creature, along with a dozen more barges belonging to Siamese Courtiers, stood ready while the Governors of Bangkok and Phetchaburi formally invited him to join the parade that would transport him upriver to the Capital.

King Narai may not have been ready to embrace the Catholic Faith, but he took delight in welcoming the French Embassy. He had commissioned a series of rest houses, built at distances of five leagues along the riverbanks, a task which was said to have taken the labour of 20,000 men. Each rest house, painted red in honour of the Ambassador and constructed of bamboo and raised on stilts, boasted three adjoining galleries; one for the reception, one the Apartment of His Excellency, and the third for his Gentlemen. Throughout there were Chinese beds, Japanese screens, Persian carpets, and provision for dinners for up to thirty guests who were served in the European style.

As the procession made its way up the Maenam River, more and more boats joined the flotilla until they numbered 100 or more, their gilded prows and coloured pennants clear against the river-banks, and the birds of variously coloured plumage that flitted all about mirrored the glory of the waterborne pageant. The river was everywhere about a quarter of a league wide, often more, and reaching back from the banks was a broad landscape of rice fields.

"This is all indeed truly magnificent, faultless in execution and glorious in the physical setting," the Abbé de Choisy remarked to the Bishop of Metellopolis as he sat back in his barge. "But why is it that no ordinary boats are to be seen on this wide river, not a single fisherman, and almost no one in the villages. It seems astonishing desolation, does it not?"

"Ordinarily the river is covered with boats," the Bishop replied. "And the villages are well populated. If we see no one, it is out of Respect for the Ambassador. It is the same when the King passes; no one shows his face and one sees only those who have not had time to hide."

The Abbé was most impressed at this, and was much pleased at the way in which the Embassy was being received in Siam.

Three days after setting out from Bangkok , the flotilla reached the last rest house, situated three-quarters of a league below Ayut-thaya, where de Chaumont was to await his Audience with King Narai.

Ayutthaya
15th October, 1685

Attentive in all my preparations, I called on the Ambassador after dinner last night, and the two of us were in conference for three hours during which agreement was reached on many things relating to the Entry into the Capital and the Royal Audience, although some difficulties remained that I said I dare not resolve, and about which I must consult with the King.

I considered the man must be mad as I listened to de Chaumont describe his Mission and its aim to convert King Narai to Catholicism, a task for which he is now asking my help.

These are dangerous waters, indeed. Why, the attachment of the Siamese to the Lord Buddha is so strong, and so inextricably linked to the Crown, that if Narai converts he must surely lose the Throne and so bring about my ruin.

I was diplomatic with the Ambassador; speaking my true mind would help no one, and the truth would be unpalatable to the

Frenchman. "Your Excellency, Most Exalted Ambassador," I addressed him. "You do me more honour than I deserve. I will be delighted to serve you and will do everything in my power to help you achieve the object of your mission."

De Chaumont was well pleased, believing I spoke of his ultimate aim, whereas I was for the moment more mindful of settling details of protocol, fearing the Ambassador would not willingly submit himself to the accepted Siamese ways, especially prostrating oneself before the Monarch as is expected of everyone. But when His Excellency showed me the address he proposed to deliver to Narai, I explained it would be politic initially to speak of the more congenial subject of friendship between France and Siam, he stamped his foot like a thwarted child. "No! The text will be as I have written."

It appears de Chaumont was equally determined to have his way in using the Bishop of Metellopolis and not me as his interpreter at his Audience with the King. But on this point I was insistent that it should be me, since His Majesty has placed me in full charge of all arrangements for the French Embassy. De Chaumont had little choice but to accept, ungraciously remarking that it is well that I am a Catholic.

25

The Court Astrologers deemed 18th October, 1685 as the most auspicious day for the King's Reception of the French Embassy, though that did not keep worry from clouding de Chaumont's face as he adjusted a lace cravat tightly. He smoothed out his silken hose; buttoned his knee-length, embroidered cloth-of-gold coat; and, reaching for a broad feathered hat and for his sword—the wearing of which at Court, Phaulkon had secured a Royal Dispensation—he sent a servant to fetch de Choisy, who shortly appeared dressed in a black satin cassock and surplice with a great mantle on top.

With the Abbé watching, de Chaumont took the Letter from the Most Christian King and placed it in a golden box. This he put into a gold cup and set upon a salver, likewise of gold, and displayed it on a table as forty Mandarins came up to pay their respects to the Ambassador and more especially—which irritated de Chaumont—

to the Letter in front of which they prostrated themselves. After the Mandarins had left, de Chaumont placed the salver with the Letter in the Abbé's hands and the two walked to where their barges were waiting.

There were separate vessels for the Letter, the Ambassador, and the Abbé, as well as four boats for the Ambassador's companions, secretary, household staff, and twenty persons in handsome livery that the Siamese found most beautiful. Finally the procession, followed by barges of all the nations, set off towards the city as trumpets and conch shells echoed across the water. There were sixty men on each side of the barges with small gilded oars, which all struck and rose from the water in unison, and in the sunlight it made an impressive sight.

Arrived at the Island City, the French party disembarked and de Chaumont was borne in State on an open gilded chair carried by ten men. De Choisy followed on a palanquin with eight bearers, and so grand was the occasion that he believed he had become the Pope. The remainder of the entourage came on horseback, the whole triumphal procession passed down a long street between two double rows of soldiers wearing helmets and carrying gilded shields, their ranks broken intermittently by war elephants in battle harness.

At the outer gate of the Palace, de Chaumont alighted from his palanquin and took the letter from its own carriage. The whole party then walked solemnly through a series of courtyards in the first two of which a regiment of 1,000 men seated in rows of six, and a squadron of some 300 horses and elephants formed a guard of honour. At the innermost court, the Ambassador and his party, led by Phaulkon, passed through a throng of Mandarins, their faces bowed to the ground, and proceeded to a short flight of steps that led to the Audience Chamber, where de Chaumont and Phaulkon stopped to allow the French Gentlemen to enter first and be seated on carpets, it having been allowed that they may enter, contrary to Siamese custom, with their heads raised in the French Manner and wearing their shoes.

As a signal that the King was about to appear, trumpets and drums sounded from within, and others outside answered. Immediately, Phaulkon removed his shoes and climbed the stairs on his knees, reminding de Choisy of pilgrims on the Scala Santa in Rome, although he thought the Greek performed much more respectfully. De Chaumont followed, accompanied by the Abbé who carried Louis XIV's Letter. He removed his hat at the topmost step and entered the chamber.

As soon as he saw King Narai, de Chaumont bowed deeply in the French Manner and, accompanied on his left by de Choisy, walked into the middle of the chamber between two rows of prostrate Mandarins, without shoes or stockings but otherwise magnificently dressed and each with a box of arrack, betel, and tobacco, the beauty of which denoted their Rank. The Ambassador was shocked to see King Narai raised high on a balcony well above head height, as he had proposed to hand the Letter to Narai and not, as Phaulkon had said he must, offer it in a shallow dish which he was expected to raise up to the King on a stick, feeling this was beneath the dignity of an Envoy of Europe's Most Christian King. He let none of this show in his face, and once standing before Narai, he embarked upon the reading of his address, uttering only the first word before he sat down and put on his hat again and continued speaking. De Choisy remained standing, still holding the Letter.

"Sire! The King, my Master, so famed throughout the world for His Great Victories, and for the Peace he has so frequently established with his enemies and at the head of his armies, has commanded me to come to Your Majesty . . ." At the word 'Majesty,' de Chaumont raised his hat briefly, as he did at every subsequent mention of the King. He continued to say that King Louis XIV presented his Marks of Esteem and assured the Great Monarch of Siam of his friendship, although nothing was more likely to unite these two sovereigns than to live in the Consciousness of the Same Belief. He added that Louis XIV beseeched him to consider that the Supreme Majesty with which he was invested could be held only from the True God who governs Heaven and Earth. . . .

De Chaumont concluded his address by saying that the most agreeable news which he could carry to his master, King Louis, would be that His Majesty, persuaded by the Truth, would take instruction in the Christian Faith.

The discourse over, the Ambassador, without standing, introduced the Abbé de Choisy and then the French Gentlemen, after which Phaulkon immediately prostrated himself, bowing his head three times before translating into Siamese de Chaumont's address.

Phaulkon spoke fast and fluently, but not so fast and so fluently that the Bishop of Metellopolis, kneeling only a little way behind him, could not hear distinctly that no word about the Christian Faith and how King Narai's Tuition in it would so greatly please Louis XIV entered the Greek's translation.

Phaulkon merely mouthed flowery platitudes.

After the interpretation was over, not appreciably shorter than the original, as Phaulkon had added many pretty phrases of his own, the Ambassador rose and took off his hat, respectfully acknowledged King Louis' Letter, took it, and moved towards the Throne. He hesitated a moment and then, appearing to have made a decision, he placed the letter on the shallow dish and raised it towards Narai only as far as he could without bending his elbow. It was still below the Monarch.

"Lift it up, lift it up!" whispered Phaulkon crawling behind de Chaumont. But the Ambassador would do no such thing, and Narai was obliged to lean half out of the window to receive the Letter, which he did laughing, the diamonds at his neck and wrists flashing in the light as he moved forward.

De Choisy breathed a sigh of relief.

De Chaumont, so pleased with his success in upholding the Honour of France, looked smug as he sat down. He promised himself that he would have an engraving made when he returned to Paris to immortalize his unbending action, along with the servile attitude of Phaulkon at his feet.

Phaulkon, too, relaxed, content that all went mostly to design.

After Narai had exchanged civilities with his pompous guest, trumpets were sounded to mark the end of the Audience, and a curtain was drawn across the window screening the King from view.

As they were leaving the chamber, de Chaumont said haughtily to Phaulkon, "I was embarrassed seeing the King's Throne so high. We had clearly resolved that I should not have to raise my arm when giving the Letter. I would have been in despair if I had displeased His Majesty."

"Sir, I was still more embarrassed," returned the Greek. "You had only one king to satisfy; I had two."

Ayutthaya
21st November, 1685

Banquets of European dishes and French wines; Siamese
dancers, their movements as graceful as their costumes are gor-
geous; lavish gifts of porcelain, of silk, of lacquer, of gold; excursions
along limitless watery passages running between rows of wooden
houses on stilts and shaded by trees in which a thousand birds sing;
elephants magnificently regaled. . . . I have lavished unerring and
unending entertainments on de Chaumont, leaving him amazed
and captivated against his sober will by the colour, the splendour,
the perfection of it all, unmatched in his experience. And still he is
a disappointed man.

26

The day after de Chaumont had his Third Audience with King Narai, Phaulkon arranged for him to see a fight staged between elephants and a tiger. Seated in stands overlooking the Royal Elephant Stockade, built of thick teak piles sunk into the ground and firmly tied, the French party watched as a tiger paced angrily across the beaten earth floor, whipping its tail and snarling as it turned and looked towards three elephants whose mahouts kept them steady against the timber wall. The face of each beast was covered by a leather mask, and behind this the animals curled up their trunks, away from their tusks.

At a word of command from the mahouts, the elephants attacked with their tusks, charging the big cat. The first elephant caught the tiger broadside and hurled it into the air. Maddened, the animal leapt at the leather mask only to be shaken loose. It bit the leg of one elephant, which bellowed in pain.

Gradually the attacks of the tiger weakened and the wretched beast was repeatedly tossed between the elephants which pushed hard, responding to the urges of their mahouts. Finally, either exhausted or too cowardly to continue, the tiger gave up and appeared dead. One of the elephants approached to turn the animal over gently, and twice the cat picked itself up until collapsing for the last time.

In the final stages of the unequal contest, in which de Chaumont had quickly lost all interest, the Ambassador turned to Phaulkon: "Like the tiger, Lord Wichayen, we make no progress. King Louis would be prepared to do much for Siam, but I am not here to ready the country for war. My mission is to declare Louis' Desire that Narai embrace Christianity. I meet him in Private Audience and what do I hear—the Dutch, always the Dutch. He tells me how he believes the Dutch are preparing an attack upon Siam; how they have become jealous by his Desire for close alliance with France, and how they are cunning and will surely thwart the French Company's Trade in Siam, what little it is, as he did not fail to remark. Yes, yes, we can address all those matters, but when I tell him my mission is to request that he take instruction in the Christian Religion, he withdraws without replying."

The suddenness of this tirade shocked Phaulkon, so rudely did it intrude into the entertainments he had arranged for his guests' pleasure. He remained courteous but made it plain that he was unprepared to indulge de Chaumont.

"Your Excellency," Phaulkon said, "please appreciate the concern of the Siamese People regarding the Dutch. It is their wish to take concerted action with the King of France in this matter, and, if you, Your Excellency, had full authority from King Louis, they could proceed to conclude such an alliance forthwith."

"I have full authority to seek the King's conversion, and I urgently ask you to press for this above all else," de Chaumont retorted.

The Greek remained firm and replied, "With respect, Sir, this I cannot do, and I most strongly urge you not to press me. Even if His Majesty were ready to embrace Christianity, I would not advise him to do so, for it could spark a Great Uprising in the country. Only if a significant number of his subjects had converted to the Faith could King Narai safely embrace Catholicism. Beware, there are others who would be king, waiting only an excuse to depose Narai.

"Your memorandum regarding trade and, more emphatically, religion which you kindly promised the King, and which I have personally relayed to him, with considerable eloquence I might add, has not met with the response you must have desired. I humbly admit that when I translated and discussed the memorandum with His Majesty, I spoke boldly for the first time about your True Mission, that of his conversion. He listened to all I had to say without interruption, and when I had finished he pondered deeply before replying, desiring me to translate his words and put them in writing to you."

Phaulkon held out his hand to his servant who passed him a folded document. "Allow me to read exactly the King's Words," he said, leafing through the pages until he came to the passage he wanted.

"This is His Majesty's Reply to the question of his conversion: 'I regret, however, that my excellent friend the King of France, has proposed to me a thing so difficult. I refer myself to the Wisdom of the Most Christian King, who can judge of the importance and of the difficulties of a matter so delicate as the change of a religion acknowledged and followed uninterruptedly throughout the Kingdom for the space of 2,229 years.'"

Smiling at the Ambassador, who stared blankly, Phaulkon added, "Your Excellency, it might make you feel easier to know that the Persian Ambassador is also seeking the King's conversion, but His Majesty has intimated to me alone that if he were to adopt another Faith, it would certainly not be Mohammedanism."

The Greek chuckled, but de Chaumont was in no mood for levity. He snatched the King's Speech from Phaulkon's hands and scanned the page, letting fall a lace handkerchief that he had been flapping to cool his face as he read and comprehended the forcefulness of Narai's Reasoned Argument as to the difficulties of changing his religion, which concluded with the comment that "if the Creator had so willed it, all nations would have had the same religion."

De Chaumont, red in the face, restrained himself with difficulty until he had finished reading. "You, Phaulkon, you! Why did you not speak of my mission earlier to His Majesty. Why did you not translate my speech to the letter. You were supposed to have prepared the way for me. You knew what our goal was. You have deceived me. You, you . . ."

De Chaumont abandoned his cold reserve and ranted unintelligibly in French, pouring out his anger and frustration on Phaulkon.

"Sir, pray calm yourself," urged the Greek, looking anxiously about, afraid that this outburst was drawing the attention of the Mandarins who were now watching two elephants in mock battle. "This is a most difficult matter, yet one that may not be altogether hopeless. I assure you that I am working wholeheartedly towards achieving the goal of your Holy Enterprise, but as I have always cautioned, we must plan our moves carefully. I suggest that before attempting the conversion of the King, we should first try to convert as many of the Siamese people as possible, along with some of the Mandarins. This we may proceed with at once, and I am sure His Majesty will not disapprove of our actions. Then, with time, the ultimate result of our endeavours is without question."

The Ambassador stared hard at Phaulkon, then stood up and, without speaking further, walked away from the stockade, leaving de Choisy to conclude the delicate situation.

The Abbé, who throughout the conversation had merely interpreted the Ambassador's French into Portuguese for Phaulkon's convenience, now turned to the Greek and spoke frankly. "Look, my good fellow, let's have no more nonsense about this. I suspect your Primary Aim is to secure an alliance between France and Siam, which I can understand. The Dutch are indeed powerful, and it would suit King Narai to have France as an ally. I am charged by our Most Christian King with the religious instruction of your Master, but as you may have possibly discerned, I am not a man who shackles himself to a lost cause. Why, Narai could ponder his conversion indefinitely once he has secured a treaty with us.

"You are a straightforward man, Phaulkon. And so am I. Tell me plainly, there is considerable doubt over the feasibility of the King changing his religion, is there not? I imagine there would be widespread unrest among the people should he do so. Am I right?"

"Most certainly you are right," Phaulkon answered almost with a sigh of relief, as if a burden had dropped from his shoulders. "Indeed, let us speak frankly and not in that roundabout fashion the Siamese so love. Yes, as matters stand at present, I should say His Majesty would never adopt a new religion. If by some extraordinary turn of events he should be urged to do so, it is my opinion that the Church in Siam would be the first to suffer in the people's rage that would most surely result. No, the only way, as I have said, is to make popular the Faith by converting as many of the Siamese as possible and let the King's conversion follow naturally. Church and State are very much one with the Siamese, far more so than in Europe."

De Choisy nodded in agreement and said, "I must admit—and I do not think I am betraying my duty to our Ambassador when I say so—that I consider Chevalier de Chaumont has been impetuous and unyielding in pushing for King Narai's conversion. Clearly the situation is more delicate than he is prepared to admit. Let us, however, not abandon all hope. Our true path forward, I humbly suggest, would be to petition the King, asking that our priests be granted concessions. Hence they may work better towards establishing our Faith in the Land."

Phaulkon smiled at de Choisy, his eyes bright as he sensed triumph. "That is, I do believe, our true way forward," he said. "And if it be made known," he added craftily, "that Louis XIV reciprocates King Narai's Friendship, and that France and Siam are seen as allies, all may be most cordially agreed. His Majesty has summoned me to advise on the Cambodian Problem, so I will take the opportunity to suggest the granting of concessions without delay."

Bangkok
21st December, 1685

The French Embassy sails for France tomorrow, carrying with it 300 bales of gifts for King Louis XIV and his Courtiers at Versailles, as well as three Siamese Ambassadors led by Kosa Pan.

I went onboard the ship this morning to present de Chaumont with the agreement we have concluded. I found the Ambassador looking drowsy. I could not discern whether it was because of the heat, oppressive for Europeans even in this our coolest month, or out of weariness after nearly three months in Siam engaged in a Mission that is, from his point of view, a failure.

"So this is it," he said with no enthusiasm when I handed him the two Treaties, one for commerce and the other of religious matters, signed by myself a little while previously, in which King Narai is pleased to grant the French concessions in respect of the friendship now forged between the two nations. The French gains are slight enough—favourable treatment of missionaries and their converts . . . free right of trade with exemption of all duties . . . rights to trade in Junkceylon . . . the right to established a fortified factory at Singora. Nothing too generous, but for me it is a step towards the alliance I seek.

De Chaumont sighed as he scanned the document and said nothing. To compensate for his superiors' lack of manners, de Choisy thanked me and shook my hand with a firm grasp. "Let us be content, he said. "There is no more to be done here now. Pray fair winds for us, my dear Phaulkon."

27

Following the departure of the French Embassy, Phaulkon proceeded to the Capital. At dinner on the night of his return, he appeared to Maria preoccupied when she had expected him triumphant at his success in conducting the negotiations with the French.

"Is the food not to your liking?" she asked.

"What?" he asked absently. "No . . . I mean yes, it's excellent as always." But he pushed his plate aside and, dismissing the servants, he turned towards Maria.

"I must unburden myself. Things are more tangled than you imagine. The treaty I signed with the French is not sufficient in itself. I need more from France; civilian and administrative support, also a small garrison, to secure my plans. If that fool de Chaumont was not so stuffy and so stuck on his ridiculous goal to convert Narai, I might have got more. As it is, I have given him a treaty that will do for now—though I admit, and I swear you to secrecy, that the King knows nothing of it, and I will never make the terms public; they would seem much too much to favour the French for the Mandarins' liking.

"Still I need more. De Chaumont is too bitter at his failure to be any use. Besides, he says he has no instructions other than to attempt Narai's conversion. Who needs instructions? Our own Embassy to France has now gone with de Chaumont, but official channels are no good to me—too much time, too much talking. Listen . . . let me tell the scheme I've set in motion."

Phaulkon rose from the table and held out his hand to escort Maria to a sofa. Laying back at ease, he smiled at his wife and began to explain what he had done:

"You'll recall Father Tachard, perhaps the keenest mind among our French guests. He was always quiet, leaving all the talking to de Chaumont and de Choisy, but I watched him closely and saw how astute he was and how he could be of service to me. We spoke amongst ourselves frequently and we became quite amicable so that I have entrusted him secretly to further my aims when he is returned to France. He is, of course, greatly flattered.

"He's a Jesuit, and while they are not of the same mind as the missionaries, it is the Jesuits who, I know, have the ear of King Louis. So I have licensed him to act independently of and unknown to the Siamese Ambassadors who accompany his return, proposing that he talks with Louis' confessor, Père de la Chaise, and hopefully later with the Pope, with the aim of getting France to dispatch some sixty or seventy good men of independent means—no salaried men— who can take up voluntary service with the State and thus work towards establishing the Christian Religion throughout the Land. This path, by subtly subverting Buddhism, I have suggested, is the best and only way of converting the King to the Faith."

Maria sat quietly, becoming fearful as she listened to his talk. Only when Phaulkon paused did she dare speak. "My dear Constance, what you suggest is Most Perilous, as you more than anyone must know. As a Catholic, I laud any plan to spread the Faith, but Buddhism is so very deeply rooted among the Siamese; it is the very air they breathe. Nothing will ever change that. We could never progress beyond more than a few converts. Even if the King wishes to convert, which in spite of his friendship towards you, I cannot believe, he would never survive should he do so. The Mandarins would kill him and all those close to him. For the sake of our son and our love, I beg you abandon this madness."

"My love, my love. Pray have faith in me. Of course, Narai will never convert, nor would I ever persuade him to do so. That would be treason, not to say impractical, and I value dearly my own fair skin."

Phaulkon smiled indulgently at Maria. "No, the question is one of power, not of religion, of Siam's Sovereignty, and my own humble role in the King's Service. Siam needs the French—its military, not its missionaries. Without their presence the Dutch will surely overwhelm us. That is why I have told Tachard to urge the French to garrison Singora as soon as possible. I have also planted the seeds in his mind that it may soon be possible to station a few French troops in Bangkok. Then, with that and with our friend White in Mergui, our trade will be protected and prosper.

"There is only one weakness I fear, and that's Chevalier de Forbin. Although he was due to return with the Embassy, the King asked for a military expert to be left behind, and he asked particularly that de Forbin be appointed. Actually it was I who suggested him; he dislikes me and is suspicious of my plans for Siam, so I thought it safer to have him here where I can watch him, rather than he return with de Chaumont and perhaps prejudice me in the minds of the French."

"Oh, Phaulkon, you know I have a true wife's faith in all that you do. Your esteem in this Land is second to none, and your Ambition has brought you great success. Let it be enough."

"Is it ever enough?" Phaulkon replied. "Yet enough for now. Come, my love, let us retire for the night. I am exhausted after these months of hosting de Chaumont. The pieces are in play; now it is sufficient to await results."

Ayutthaya
7th January, 1686

Out of another's failure it is often possible to make great personal gain. This I have managed with comparative ease in my negotiations with the French, while de Chaumont, by contrast, has left virtually empty handed. Narai is greatly pleased with what I have won for Siam, the basis for a much desired Siamese-Franco alliance without great concessions in return, and henceforth he is well disposed to all that I might think or suggest.

In his gratitude, however, the Siamese Monarch is not blind to the precarious position into which I, his favourite, have manoeuvred myself, and he is conscious of the jealousies among his Courtiers. He tells me that at his farewell Audience with de Chaumont he had described me as a Faithful Servant and asked the Ambassador to recommend me to King Louis so that I might find a country of safety should I be forced to flee Siam.

The King a true patron. I a faithful servant.

But who in his own eyes is as others see him?

The Mohammedans despise me and want revenge for the influence they have lost at my hand; the English too, despise me; de Chaumont thinks me too clever by half; and the Siamese Mandarins hold me in envy and fear. Perhaps the King has more foresight than I in seeking to find a refuge for me in France.

Yet I am not alarmed, nor ready to seek refuge. I am concerned, nonetheless, that in preoccupying myself with the French Embassy for the past months, I have let other matters drift. I am like a juggler keeping half a dozen balls in the air at once.

The French are well poised, ready to fortify Singora as protection to the tin trade in the South, and if Tachard does his work, I will have, before too long, Frenchmen in Bangkok as well. The English have been put in their place, but need watching as an offensive by them would be disastrous. The Siamese situation is, as always, delicate.

And there is Samuel White at Mergui, and that is what worries me most. It should be the least of my cares—my own people in position by My Authority—but reviewing dispatches from my spies at the port, they are behaving without proper restraint, threatening to unbalance my whole stratagem. It is solely due to me that White can view Mergui as his own domain, but the reports reaching me leave no doubt to that fact that not everyone in Mergui is enamoured with the Englishman. My close watch is required and I will rein him in if need be.

28

A delegation of Mohammedan traders from Mergui arrived in Ayutthaya to demand something be done to control White. It put its case before the Mandarins, and a violent argument broke out between the Siamese, who by tradition supported the Mohammedans, and Phaulkon, White's benefactor and he who had secured Royal Sanction for attacks against Golconda.

"What he's done is not proper," spoke a white-haired Mohammedan merchant, the patriarch of one of Mergui's oldest Indian trading houses. "White has fitted the *Prosperous* with cannon and musket that can only mean trouble. And that Captain he's hired, Coates, swaggers and grins like a pirate. I'd swear he's never done a day's honest trade in his entire life. If he's going to make war on Golconda and Ava, it will destroy our trade. The losses will be enormous. It's insane and must be stopped."

Phaulkon argued in vain that Siam was incurring unacceptable losses in revenues due to the actions of Golconda, and the problem must be tackled firmly and Siam assert its authority.

The Mandarins, however, were less interested in Mergui and more in using the opportunity to attack the Greek, and so vehement were they in their outcry against his actions that King Narai was forced to rule against his Favourite.

When the news of this reached Mergui, White was outraged and cursed the Siamese. Yet he had faith in Phaulkon's power, and he continued to believe the Greek could and would continue to protect him, and so he ignored Ayutthaya's ruling against his actions and proceeded as planned, sure that Phaulkon would calm any troubled waters. To cover himself, he sent two letters to Captain Coates; one letter contained the orders from Ayutthaya that he desist, the other a personal note telling him to ignore the former and continue as planned. Phaulkon was informed of this but felt it was not yet time for him to intervene.

Coates had a boyish spirit of adventure that, inspired by White, overcame his weak character and sense of insecurity. The spirits of all in Mergui, however, were sadly affected by little Thomas Ivatt's sudden death from fever, and it was not until the passing of this friend had been suitably mourned that Coates made preparations and put to sea. His first action was to sail up the river near the port of Narsapore and seize the treasure ship *New Jerusalem* and its cargo of, among other valuables, rubies. The prize should have been sufficient—it could have bought Coates respectability and a country estate in England—yet he was a poor pirate and wished to cloak his actions with an air of legitimacy, and hence proceeded to blockade Madapollam at the bar of the river, and seized and torched the rice boats that attempted to pass in a show of all-out war against Golconda. It was a foolish act with possibly disastrous consequences. The English Company was immediately angered, and dispatched a sloop from Madras to take Coates. Fortunately for him, Madras was seventy leagues distant, and before the ship could reach him, he had made a settlement with local Company Officials, returning most of the valuables he had seized and so managing to reduce a bill for losses and damages from 565,000 English pounds to 17,533 pounds.

The enormity of what Coates had won and lost threw White into a fury when he heard of it. He could only hope that the 300 leagues that separated the scene of Coates' piracy from Ayutthaya would be sufficient to give him time to conjure an excuse by which he could justify his recklessness and disobedience to Phaulkon. Even apart from Coates' escapades, White's own actions were getting him into deeper waters.

While Coates was at Madapollam, White decided to take whatever prizes he could, and dispatched another filibuster, Captain Cropley, who commanded the *Dorothy*, to prowl the Bay of Bengal. When a ship belonging to Masulipatam was captured by Cropley, White had it re-named the *Revenge*, re-fitted as a frigate under the command of a Captain English, and added to his now growing fleet of armed vessels sailing out of Mergui.

Together, the *Dorothy* and the *Revenge* were scouring the Coast of Pegu when they spotted the merchantman *Traja Raja* and seized her. The ship was sailing out of Burma, and Cropley and English took her to be fair game in spite of being told by the well-to-do Hindu merchants they found onboard that the ship belonged to an Indian merchant who was a resident of Madras and enjoyed the protection of the English Company there. The Indians' complaints were ignored, and when Cropley and English brought the *Traja Raja* into Mergui, White locked them in a storehouse and left them there without food or drink. Passersby could hear their cries for help, but only on the eighth day did White release them on condition that they paid 1,350 pounds and signed a statement that nothing had been taken from them and they had not been harmed.

White was now the master of the Bay of Bengal. He took care to protect the private trade of the Company's factors in Madras, while Cropley and English preyed on Indian shipping, seizing seven vessels in six months, aside from the numerous ships that chose to pay a heavy toll to avoid seizure. So extensive were his operations that White saw the need to employ a secretary, and when fate brought Francis Davenport, an adventurer and sailor, into his realm he offered the man a handsome salary to organize his affairs. In the way of fate, Davenport, a native of Boston with a dubious reputation that was perhaps blacker than the truth, had first sailed to the East in 1670 aboard the *Hopewell* in which Phaulkon was at that time serving as a seaman and White's brother, George, was a passenger.

Although White was an Official of the Siamese, the returns from his filibustering did little to swell the Royal Coffers; the Treasury did receive some revenue and Phaulkon received a portion, but White, presumably thinking Ayutthaya would never know, salted away the lion's share for himself, which further intensified the hatred of every Mohammedan trader in Mergui.

Ayutthaya
30th March, 1686

Shortly I will have to take White to task for abusing my authority. He is arousing enormous animosity which rebounds on me, and in many peoples' eyes we are two of a kind. I remember it was Strangh who called White "this creature" of mine. I resent this bitterly. English Company men see us as pure adventurers bent on personal gain, while the Siamese typically view all foreigners as contemptible and never to be trusted. In reality, White and I are utterly dissimilar, and what characteristics we may have in common—certainly Courage, Ambition, and Wits quick enough to pursue that ambition—are outweighed by the differences in our natures.

White operates with a total disregard for Legitimacy, desiring nothing more than to enrich himself quickly and retire. White plans to return to England; my place is here.

29

Matters with White came to the boil shortly after the monsoon broke in 1686. The Englishman's filibustering in the Bay of Bengal had by then become too much for Phaulkon to tolerate, as his own position was threatened by the Mohammedan's bitter complaints to King Narai against White. Phaulkon realized that to ensure his own safety he would have to distance himself from White, let it be seen that he alone was accountable for his actions. At the same time, he wished to keep him loyal as a friend, as an ally to guard Mergui.

Seeing no other safe course, Phaulkon wrote to White summoning him to Louvo to face an Official Enquiry into his conduct as Customs Master of Mergui. The letter was couched in terms that were stern but not sufficient to cause undue alarm.

ф

"Look at this," White said flinging the letter down in front of Davenport. "Damn them all. They cannot summons me."

Davenport picked up the letter and read it before speaking: "Sam, you forget you are employed by the King of Siam," he said. "You cannot ignore it, not unless you're planning to flee. And look, Phaulkon makes no specific accusations against you. I'd say it was a typical Oriental ploy to appease the Mandarins; all show, no substance.

"Aye, you may be right. I can rely on Phaulkon's protection."

"Besides, Sam, it's not a good time to antagonize the Siamese. There's still ill-feeling about the Company overcharging Narai for that consignment of rubies. It's not our fault, but they'll damn all the English for it."

φ

White resigned himself to answer Phaulkon's summons and, taking with him Davenport, whom he considered more an advisor than a secretary, particularly in critical affairs that demanded diplomacy, he set out from Mergui on 20th May and made good time to Ayutthaya, harried as he was along the way by Phaulkon's messengers, and reached the Capital in 12 days.

The journey, variously by boat, elephant, and sedan chair, was not without mishap, however. Sudden squalls of drenching rain followed by a sharp drop in temperature increased the danger of chills and fever, while making mosquitoes all the more prevalent.

Arrived in Ayutthaya, White came down with malaria and travelled wearily the additional leagues upriver to Louvo, where a raging fever drove him to his sick bed.

Several weeks passed and never once did Phaulkon send to enquire after White's health, though Maria did provide him with things that she thought might be grateful to him and proper for him. Yet, when feeling a little better, White came to Phaulkon's gates and sent in his name, the Greek's servants turned him away.

A little while after, White was then taken sick again, this time with stomach pains, and alarmed at his friend's seeming desertion, he wrote to Phaulkon saying that as he had "one foot in the grave" he wanted to "safely aver (and nothing troubles my conscience now so much as that) how I have always been more Zealous for the Honour and Interest of my Master the King than in my Devotion towards my creator, under whose afflicting Hand I now lie."

The point of the letter came in its conclusion, where White asked how he had offended Phaulkon, and said he would throw himself at his friend's mercy, confident that he would not "take delight in plucking down the Building which your own hand had raised."

Phaulkon had purposely ignored White during his illness in order to put some distance between them in the eyes of the Mandarins, and on receipt of his letter he proposed to make a studied response so as to clarify both their positions.

His reply was a remarkable document. Clearly written with the hope or intention that it would be read by others, it revealed as much about Phaulkon's perception of his own Status as of his relationship with White:

Right Worshipful,

We know of no reason you have to charge us with Strangeness in our deportment to you, when you consider or observe our general Carriage towards all other persons, which we hope is not offensive to any man in particular. The jealousies you express of having private Enemies, who endeavour to estrange us from you, as 'tis on our part altogether Causeless; so it not only argues you culpable of something you would not have discovered, but highly reflects upon us, as if we took pleasure in harkening to the malicious tattling and detraction of over busie men, to the prejudice of those we have thought worthy of so considerable Trust, as we, upon mature deliberation, thought good to confer upon you: Nay, Sir, we must be plain, and tell you. The Shahbandar has no other

Enemy, that we know of, than the Shahbandar, which your own hand will evidently make appear.

That you are now reduced so near the grave is a matter of trouble to us, and that you may not hasten yourself thither, let us, as your Friend, persuade you to Temperance. As for the Protestation you make of your Zeal for His Majesty's Honour and Interest, give us leave to tell you, that it is no miracle to see a man drive on his own Covetous designs, under a pretext of promoting his King's interest, though we do not desire to charge you with being a Court Parasite.

The satisfaction you desire shall be granted to you, so soon as you are in a condition to be Examined by our Secretary, who should long since have been sent to you, had we not understood your Indisposition, and be cautioned to be plain, fair and moderate in your Answers, to whatever Queries he proposes to you; avoiding all Passionate Expressions or Gestures, which may do you much harm, but cannot avail anything to your advantage.

It will be no small pleasure to us to find you as innocent as you pretend, nor shall we ever take delight to ruin what our hands have built up; but if we perceive a Structure of our own raising begin to totter, and threaten our own ruine with its fall, none can tax us with imprudence, if we take it down in time. There is your own Metaphor restored, and the needful in Answer to your letter of yesterday's date, concluded with our hearty wishes for your recovery, as being

Your friend,
Phaulkon.

White fell back on the pillows after scanning the letter. He looked up at Davenport and moaned, "'We, we, we.' What does he mean? Has power gone to his head that he thinks himself a king? Arrogant bastard. God, if I had the strength I'd return to Mergui and damn his bloody enquiry."

Louvo
15th July, 1686

This day was White's hearing at the Palace. Until now, I had refused to see him since he arrived at Louvo a sick man—though I made sure I was kept fully informed about the state of his health— as I wanted him to have leisure in which to Reflect on his Position. He must have been aware that he had stepped outside his bounds in his filibustering and could be sent to gaol, and he would be anxious to Secure his Liberty. This would be especially worrying to him in Louvo where, unlike in Mergui with a ship always to hand, there is no immediate means of escape.

I was not surprised, therefore, to be greeted by a fearful and dejected White this morning as we met to attend the Committee of Enquiry. Sunken eyes in a pale and drawn face showed his nerve was all but broken.

Had I been unnecessarily cruel?

The Committee I had convened consisted of only myself and the next most senior Mandarin, and White's manner revived when he realized he would not have to face an Inquisition. I had made sure all the documents concerning the case were in English, and these I kept shuffling so that those that might prove difficult for White to answer were never presented in the course of the examination.

White was able to assume a Penitent Air, and after due deliberation the Committee found him innocent of any wrongdoing.

When it was over, I called him aside. "Well, Sir, you are cleared," I told him. "But you must know that you owe your escape to me as I owe myself and all I have to your good brother, George. If I have frowned on you, be satisfied that I have reason. I make no doubt that your accounts, if thoroughly scanned, would appear Notorious Unhandsome. I hope today will be a caution to you for the future. Nor are you to think that though I love you well, yet would I Ruin Myself to screen you."

White, prudent enough not to reply, bowed deeply, and I left him with the promise that we should dine together soon.

30

"The White affair is settled," Phaulkon told Maria on the morning after the hearing. During the months since the departure of the French Embassy he found himself confiding more and more in his wife, spending the early part of most evenings in her company before attending the King's Secret Council. It was not just her willingness to listen, nor even her understanding that pleased Phaulkon; it was in the calmness of her Piety that he experienced relief from the strain he had begun to feel.

"Yes, White's in the clear, for the moment," Phaulkon said, lying back on cushions while Maria sat with her embroidery. "But the farce of the Enquiry, engineered by me, will not appease the Mandarins for long. They will pounce quick enough if given another chance of catching him. White's a rogue, out for all he can get, and not caring too much how he gets it. Still, he serves our purpose for the moment.

"Indeed, I am considering elevating Samuel in Narai's Service, and think I shall detain him here until I can decide. It would please me to have the company of an Englishman, if only because it takes some of the Mandarins jealous regard away from myself.

"Besides, I owe it to brother George. He has stood by me for all his being in England. It was he who caused in me a change of heart after I purposely refused to see Samuel before his Enquiry. I had received word from George, telling me that he had distributed the gifts I sent via Father Pascot and managed to calm English tempers stirred up by Strangh. Hopefully that will stop the English from declaring war on us over White's antics in the Bay of Bengal. At least until I receive French support."

"And the French. Will they support you?" Maria asked.

"It is in their interest to send the support I have asked for. They crave more influence here, and I can give it to them. They need me and I need them. It is their soldiers who can discipline the Siamese Army for the protection of the Kingdom and, if need be, the King himself. They would be under his ultimate command, though orders would come directly through me."

"And what of the King?"

"He does not interfere. He accepts our ruling on White. He does not question my actions nor my ideas. In these matters it is I who rule."

"But why, dear Phaulkon, do you take such chances? You have achieved so much, brought so much glory on yourself, and are recognized by the Pope and by the Courts of England and France. You are not yet forty years old and we have wealth beyond our needs. Why stay here when we would be welcome in Europe where we could live our lives with ease and honour?"

"It is my Fate and I must follow my Destiny," Phaulkon replied, though he could see that his words did not satisfy Maria. He wondered if she really understood him when he himself could not give words to what fired him.

Ayutthaya
21st August, 1686

Life in Ayutthaya thrives upon intrigue, never more so than this last month when rumours of an uprising spread through the city as if someone had put a torch to a trail of gunpowder. Usually I pay little heed to such talk, as what is rumoured rarely comes to pass. It requires a more clever mind than that of the gossip to grasp the reality of power among the Siamese. But these are unusual times; I have much at stake, and my plans are at a sensitive stage, awaiting as I am for French allies to arrive.

The trouble in July worried me greatly, as it sprung in large part from those very plans I am trying to implement, and sought to attack the one person on whom the Fate of the Nation and myself hangs: the King. The plotters were my old enemies the Mohammedans.

With justification, I admit, they have always viewed me as the enemy. More so now I have placed White in Mergui. This must seem to them a conspiracy. Moreover, the Mohammedans hope that Narai might be persuaded to embrace the Koran, but he has paid more attention to the French Embassy than to the overtures of the Persian Ambassador. As is the way with people who hold grievances, whether real in their own lights or perceived as such, the Mohammedans have personified their Ill Feelings in the shape of the King and myself. They have plotted to Assassinate us both.

Their chosen weapon was the Makassars, doubtless with the connivance of some of the Mandarins. No uprising can succeed without some such support, if only tacit. These sullen, ill-natured people are natives of the Celebes to whom Narai so generously gave sanctuary after they fled their homeland, and provided land for them close by the foreign factories outside the walls of Ayutthaya. It was generous but foolhardy, for the Makassars are known and feared throughout the East for their Savagery, showing no mercy in battle as they hack their victims to death, preferring the kris over firearms, which they feel are unworthy of their valour. I say valour, yet it arises less from the heart and more from barbarity and Complete Disregard for their own lives, and is easily whipped into fury by intoxication from opium.

The Makassar Uprising was an abortive affair, but not through any lack of careful planning. Indeed, in what was a considered strategy, they intended to torch and sack Ayutthaya before marching on Louvo, overthrowing Narai, and installing one of his brothers, duly converted to Mohammedanism, on the Throne. All was set for July, and only a propitious moment for attack was awaited. Just six hours before the order was to be given, word of the insurrection reached the Governor of Ayutthaya, who quickly arrested the Makassar ringleaders.

The Governor immediately dispatched a messenger to me at Louvo, where I was accompanying His Majesty, to inform me of the State of Affairs. After ordering the defence of the Summer Capital, I made all haste to reach Ayutthaya, only to find the city calm, the rebels having dispersed once they realized their plot had been discovered and their leaders captured.

Aware of the Makassars' reputation for savouring vengeance with particular ferocity, I decided upon Moderation and Mercy in my treatment of their leaders, one of whom had threatened to fight to the death rather than suffer punishment. He was brought to me struggling in the clutches of four guards, with his hands and neck securely bound. I ordered the ropes removed, and spoke quietly, telling him he would come to no harm, nor be punished provided he make a Full Confession of the Facts leading to the aborted Uprising and name those involved. This he promised, and he was sent to the King at Louvo, and in due course my word was honoured and the man was freed.

It happened, however, that one of the other ringleaders was less trusting, and refused to be taken to Louvo, instead asking to be allowed to the leave the Kingdom. To this I agreed, but when he and some fifty of his men left in their boats, I sent orders to de Forbin, who has charge of the garrison at Bangkok, to put chains across the river and to arrest the Makassars should they attempt to pass. I made it clear that he was forbidden to let a soul know of my instructions and that the affair demanded Inviolable Secrecy for Reasons of State. That blasted Frenchman mishandled the whole episode, and if it was not for the frightful loss of life, I could almost believe he did it to make trouble for me.

According to the reports I received, the Makassars arrived at Bangkok and saw the chains preventing their passage. The Captain and seven of his men came ashore and were presented to de Forbin, who told them that because of the rebellion, of which they had undoubtedly heard, he had orders to forbid any Siamese from leaving the Kingdom. When told all passengers were Makassars returning to their homeland, de Forbin said he did not doubt the Captain's word and assured them that all would be well; nevertheless they must wait onshore until clearance was received from Ayutthaya. The Captain agreed, but said his men would all come armed, as the kris is to them a Mark of Honour. Like a fool, de Forbin agreed to let these wild natives come amongst him wearing those daggers with which a Makassar would slit a man's throat without a thought. Being new to the Orient, de Forbin holds the European soldiers' typical contempt for local weapons. A foot-long blade seems nothing to him; he was about to find out just how bloody effective they are.

He did reconsider, but it was too late. An old Portuguese soldier, whom he had instructed to disarm the Makassars once they had landed, told him that what he ordered was impossible as the Makassars were not a people to be taken; they would die first or, more likely, slay every mother's son in the garrison. De Forbin paid no heed to the advice.

By now the Makassars had landed and—still believing in fair play—de Forbin told the Siamese Mandarin, who acted as his interpreter, to inform their Captain that the orders were unfortunate but he would be well used while awaiting permission to pass. No sooner had the words been uttered—either misunderstood or unheard—than six of the Makassars drew their daggers and fell like devils upon the Mandarin and his entourage, slaughtering them all in an instant. De Forbin retreated to his group of soldiers and almost lost his life when he seized a lance and thrust it into the stomach of the foremost Makassar. The man, run though as he was, would not go down, but kept advancing, slashing with his kris. De Forbin dared neither release the lance nor pull it from the man's stomach for a second thrust, and was only relieved when others of the lancemen finally laid the man dead.

Enraged at seeing their fellows fall, the rest of the Makassars entered the bloody fray, screaming horribly as they routed de Forbin's troops. He lost 366 men before the Makassars—with only 17 dead in battle—fled into the forest. Over the next two days, de Forbin hunted them down until all were killed, no quarter being expected or given.

Word of the Bloody Fiasco in Bangkok quickly reached us in Ayutthaya and stirred up the Animosity of the many Makassars still here. We are now watching them intently, and manage to keep their restlessness in check, though I fear this will not be the end of the matter.

31

"The man would have me Assassinated, such a pitch of violence has his jealousy reached," Chevalier de Forbin declared to his adjutant after the attack of the Makassars in Bangkok. "He knew what would happen when he allowed those savages to depart Ayutthaya and then commanding me to detain them here on the river. And now he orders me to arrest the Captain of this ship moored at the bar, a ship of forty guns and ninety men. Is this madness or low cunning?"

Handsome, sharp, and ambitious, Chevalier Claude de Forbin had been a prominent figure in the French Embassy led by Chevalier de Chaumont. In this thirty-year-old Frenchman, Phaulkon recognized a like soul, a man as ambitious as himself and with the wit, boldness, and arrogance to fulfill his ambitions.

After Narai had made de Forbin Governor of Bangkok, as well as Admiral and General of the Siamese Armies, and continued to show his goodness towards him, the Frenchman saw the opportunity for his own advancement and the chance to eclipse Phaulkon.

He was careful to let no sign of animosity towards the Greek be seen. He supported him against the Mandarins when they sought to secure his downfall and accused him of the wrongful arrest of a French merchant. Yet his fiery imagination was as strong as his ambition, and he allowed himself to believe that Phaulkon—far from being grateful for service he had rendered him—hated him all the more and would have him poisoned. Thereafter he took all his meals alone.

Now in Phaulkon's order to arrest the Captain of the *Prudent Mary*, who had in some way infringed the laws of Siam, he saw yet another attempt by the Greek to put his life in jeopardy.

"'Tis an order impossible to execute," the adjutant replied after de Forbin had shown him Phaulkon's instructions.

"Precisely," said de Forbin. "But the deep meditations in which you have found me so immersed are to ascertain what course I shall take to put it into execution. I am resolved to confound Monsieur Constance forever, by letting him see that those Projects which he thinks in the main are impossible, and which he only puts upon me in hopes that I shall perish in the attempt, are not beyond my reach."

The adjutant was shocked on hearing this, and tried to dissuade his superior. "But, Sir, I beg you, do not let this Greek cloud your judgement, for surely it would be suicide to attempt to take the *Prudent Mary*, armed as she is, and . . ."

"Quiet, man. You talk to no purpose. My resolution is fixed. However, do not be downcast. I will use precaution, and I still hope to extricate myself happily from this Wicked Snare."

It later proved, when the arrest of the *Prudent Mary's* captain was effected by guile, that de Forbin's belief in himself was justified—though part of the precaution he had taken was to press the Lady Phaulkon's uncle to be a part of the arresting party.

On hearing the danger in which his wife's kinsman had been placed by de Forbin, Phaulkon was outraged.

Yet it was the Frenchman's pride that defeated him in the end, playing into Phaulkon's hands. Stung by rebukes he received from the Greek, both regarding the Makassar debacle and the *Prudent Mary* incident, de Forbin wrote to him claiming in the strongest terms that no blame be attached to him in the former, while the latter duty had been so far beneath the Dignity of his Rank that he felt compelled to Submit his Resignation.

Phaulkon accepted this readily, confident that with the imminent arrival of support from France, de Forbin could no longer thwart his schemes.

Ayutthaya
7th September, 1686

For the past few weeks I have feared that the Frenchman de Forbin would drive me to Despair. Never have I met such vanity, and thank God I am now rid of him for all my attention is taken with the Makassars, who are as tinder awaiting a spark. Quelling that first attempted Uprising has served only to incense them further. The tension mounts by the day as we ready for new attacks, the situation being all the more perilous with the King returned to Ayutthaya from Louvo, which demands ever greater precautions be taken to ensure his safety.

I have taken charge of the Operations myself. It is a serious situation, and if allowed to deteriorate, the consequences for us all—the King, myself, and everyone who wishes the Advancement of Siam—would be fatal. What makes it more difficult is that some of the Mandarins are with the Makassars, supporting their Cause for their own ends, to bring about a Court Rebellion. But I have no proof, no names. My only chance of success is to squash any uprising ere it starts.

I have given orders for the Makassar camp to be gradually and quietly surrounded by troops, but for them to remain concealed so as not to raise alarm, while I have further ordered spiked stakes be driven into the riverbed to impede any Makassar charge from their island stronghold.

In rallying our forces, I have summoned all the Europeans here to give me their support, and sixty have answered my call, including French Gentlemen and English Sea Captains, among them Captain Coates, who has not yet returned to Mergui, and Captain Udall who commands the *Herbert*. These men I can trust to fight, and I would rather have any one of them at my side in battle than a hundred Siamese. Samuel White is also still with us, and as always keen for a fight, but he remains weak from his illness and only with the utmost difficulty have I persuaded him he is unfit to do battle.

The Europeans whom I call my generals gather at my house each night to plan our campaign, though I fear it is extremely unsettling for Maria to host these men, not a few of whom are wild, uncouth characters that no Lady should be asked to entertain in her home. But she proves exceptional, and understands without explanation from me the Emergency we face. Never once does she complain, nor show fear. She trusts totally in me.

There is great tension in the city. Few traders dare go on the streets, and even the dogs lay low, slinking into corners, sensing danger.

32

On the morning of 10th September, the Prince of the Makassars, accompanied by a desperate-looking crew of supporters, all armed with krises and lances, went to the Palace gates and sent in word to King Narai that the Prince acknowledged his past errors, swore to maintain a Peaceful Demeanour in future, and so sought a Royal Pardon for which he desired to be allowed to prostrate himself at the feet of His Majesty.

The Prince's plea lacked sincerity to Phaulkon's ear, and he advised that word be sent back from the Palace that the fact that the Makassars had come armed was at odds with their words, and so first the Prince and his attendants should surrender their weapons. Once they had done so, King Narai would readily grant him liberty to enter his presence and Bestow the Pardon he requested.

So haughty and proud were these natives that the Prince, on hearing the reply from the Palace, responded angrily.

"Never will I allow my people to find me guilty of such a Base Submission as laying down my arms," he bellowed at the King's messenger. "Warn your master that I am not insensible to an approaching great storm, but know that I am like a tree, rooted firm and will endure, falling only after there may be much ruin around me. Since I am not permitted to speak to the King bearing arms, he, if he has any further business with me, knows where to find my house."

On hearing this threat, those in the Palace knew that blood would be spilled if the Prince was any further antagonized, and they bit back their resentment and permitted him to depart in peace.

An uneasy calm settled over the city after the Makassars returned to their camp, where no activity was seen for three days. Finally, Phaulkon decided to act and, under cover of darkness, he ordered the complete encirclement of the Makassar camp, using barges to block the small river that flowed past the settlement and defended it from a frontal attack.

Phaulkon's plan was to attack by boat at first light on 14th September with a force of three score Europeans and a few hundred Siamese soldiers. Half an hour before dawn, he dispatched a small advance party to set fire to the Makassar camp to force them into an open fight. He had issued his men strict orders to attempt no engagement with the Makassars until the blaze had taken hold. To his horror, so keen for a fight were some of the Europeans, that they failed to wait for the firing and paid dearly for their rashness.

Phaulkon watched helplessly as Captain Coates, a man he liked in spite of his considering him foolish for never having profitted from his filibustering, landed his squad on a dry point of land. They were quickly spotted by the Makassars who rushed from their houses and slew several of them before taking cover again in their homes. Coates himself was one of the casualties, though ironically not by the hand of the natives. In the frantic scramble to re-gain the boats, he was drowned in the river, weighed down by his weapons.

Inactivity hung heavily on Phaulkon, yet to do otherwise was folly. Until the fires and the artillery bombardment had forced the enemy into disarray, a direct attack on the Makassar's camp was impossible. Coates' men had been picked off easily before they had the field for an open engagement.

For three hours the cannon pounded the camp, and the flames began to envelop house after house so that the Makassars were driven higher up the river. Still the waiting was unbearable and, against orders, Captain Udall took his party ashore. They had scarcely landed when a group of Makassars disguised as Siamese fell upon them. Udall was one of the first to fall.

Seeing the slaughter, Phaulkon could restrain himself no longer. Casting aside reason and caution, he leapt from his boat and it was almost the last thing he ever did. Perhaps the Makassars recognized him as the leader, for immediately a group of them rushed forward with lances. Phaulkon faced them and stood his ground, though aware what folly it was to take on any Makassar in a hand-to-hand fight instead of staying back and relying on firearms. Yet his heart overruled his head. Only when he had drawn his sword did his Sensibility return and he saw how useless his position was against the lances of so many.

Luckily, before the natives came within distance, one of his slaves flung him into the water and swam with him back to the boats. Phaulkon clung on to the offside of the stern while his men fired off their muskets and blunderbusses. Even though they were at close range and disciplined in their firing, only with the greatest difficulty were the Makassars prevented from reaching them. Not a soul among Phaulkon's men had before seen such Crazed Valour, and it was if, as Samuel White later remarked, the Makassars were a sort of people who only valued their lives by the mischief they could do at their deaths.

Phaulkon escaped death only by chance, and the courage of his guard. It took him some minutes to recover his breath before he could join his men in the boats and continue the struggle. And a desperate fight it was. Four good Frenchmen were soon lost to lance thrusts, and although the musketeers kept up the firing, it was difficult to pick off the Makassars, who between forays retreated behind the riverbank's thick cover of bamboo and bush. The struggle raged for four hours before Phaulkon's position was reinforced by a large contingent of Siamese. Soon the advantage began to tell, and more and more Malays were slain until, around three in the afternoon, the Captain of Phaulkon's Guard struck a fatal blow at the Makassar Prince.

Seeing their leader dead, the fight went out of the natives and they retreated into their camp. The day was won, but at a terrible price. Much blood had been spilled, and but for the Grace of God, fortunes could have so easily been reversed, Phaulkon routed and the King taken. The Greek trembled at the thought.

At four o' clock in the afternoon, Phaulkon, accompanied by the surviving Europeans, straggled back to his house. It was not the return of victors; his shoulders sagged and fatigue wracked his whole body. He had only minor wounds, mere scratches, but the blood of others smeared his face and arms and clothes like a butcher returned from the slaughterhouse.

Hearing the men's voices, Lady Phaulkon rushed from her room and stood in the doorway, staring at the bedraggled and bloodied company. For a moment she scarcely knew whether they were flesh and bone or ghosts risen from the battlefield. Her drawn face and the dark rings under her eyes told of the sleepless night she had passed in a terrified vigil, praying as she desperately awaited news. Then, rubbing disbelief from her tired eyes, she ran to embrace her husband, kissed him and held still in his arms—arms that had so nearly failed her in providing the Protection in which she trusted.

She looked up into Phaulkon's eyes and smiled, before turning to greet his companions, shaking their hands and speaking kindly. The servants were summoned to bring food and drink, and the men fell upon the victuals with scant regard for manners.

Dearly as Phaulkon desired to stay with Maria, his duty lay with the King, and he only delayed to wash the blood from his person and don fresh attire before hurrying to the Palace, where Narai was much pleased to hear his report and learn of the Victory, promising to bestow gifts upon those who had shown their Loyalty with such valour.

Ayutthaya
21st September, 1686

The Makassar affair is not finished. The Gratitude of the
King and the relief of all of us who survived must be weighed
against the shock we have suffered. The fear and anxiety that the
rebellion has raised in all our hearts is compounded by the un-
spoken knowledge that there is a Sickness at the very Heart of the
Nation, the future is threatening. The Makassars would never have
been first so agitated and then so emboldened unless some of the
Siamese Mandarins had sworn their secret support of their Cause.

Here is more than a native uprising. A Conspiracy is abroad, and
to squash this no mercy could be shown to the Makassar survivors.
It was not sufficient to have suppressed the rebellion, the whole had
to be purged in blood least conspirators should rise again.

In battle, no quarter had been given on either side save for a boy
of some 12 years, the son of the Makassar Prince who, upon seeing
his father fall, came at me with his lance levelled. I stood my ground,

185

prepared for the attack, but at the last moment the boy's courage left him and he threw himself at my feet. Half crazed by battle as I was, I could no more slay him in cold blood than my own son, and I lifted him to his feet and had him sent to the King unfettered by chains.

I do not know what has become of the boy since, but for the rest of the Makassars an example had to be made. The lucky ones were those who chose to die rather than face capture. Those that we did take were to die horribly as a lesson to those that might support them. All captives to a man were eaten by tigers, and even that fate was refined, the beasts kept on chains so that they could just reach their victims' extremities. Only slowly were the chains slackened and the Makassars consumed alive.

Their screams return to me in nightmares. So, too, does the sight of poor Udall's body that was disinterred at night by Sorcerers, stripped naked, and bound to a tree. Even I, who have seen so much, have no comprehension of the Evil and Strangeness of these times. My body has been subject to shakes and quivers since the rebellion, and there are many moments when I wonder where I am and what I have become. It seems I am as a captive and cannot leave this place nor the work I have begun, as surely as if I am chained.

33

In the weeks following the Rebellion, Phaulkon's spirits gradually revived. The uprising had shaken everyone, and shown that there were grave weaknesses in the Security of the Kingdom. But the Greek had triumphed and his foes could see that he still held the reins of power.

He was further buoyed up by the letters from George White that Captain Udall had brought out from England and which led him to believe that, in spite of his less than cordial relations with the East India Company, his reputation in England had grown admirably.

So pleased was he with George White's efforts to represent him in a favourable light among the English, that he felt more affectionate towards his brother, Samuel, and had a mind to elevate his position in Siam.

φ

"Samuel, welcome," Phaulkon said when a servant showed the Englishman into his chamber where he was to to dine with him in private. "You look so well. Fully recovered I trust."

"Aye, Constantine, but I hurt that I missed the fight with the Makassars," White replied.

"Hush, my man. It was a despicable affair. Let us talk of more congenial matters. But first, eat. You will find my cook as wondrous as ever." Phaulkon swept an arm over a dining table laden with Chinese and European delicacies, every one presented in a golden dish, and wines and liqueurs from many different countries. "I find your brother George so fast and so true a friend to me," he continued, "that for his sake I will grant what you will. A position here at Court, perhaps?"

White appeared tired. His eyes were dull and Phaulkon noticed how little he was eating. "I desire nothing," he replied, "but liberty to return to my former station."

"'Tis a pity. I have much work and so few people I can trust here, and I had hoped you would accept the position of my assistant in Ayutthaya, with an annual remuneration of, say, 6,000 English pounds. That is surely a tempting proposition? Why, you might become the next First Minister."

White shuddered. "My Lord, you are most generous, but I do not have the talent for the work you offer. I know only of ships and trade."

Phaulkon did not give up easily, but White became more uneasy at his talk of life in the Capital and the possibilities for wealth and power that it held.

Finally, brushing aside the flask of brandy that Phaulkon was holding out, he looked directly at his host and begged to be allowed to speak freely.

"My Dear Constantine," he said, "I am truly grateful for all that you have done for me. I owe you much, on my own account and out of your friendship with my respected brother. To speak the truth, I do not feel comfortable in Ayutthaya; there is no escape save the river, and any flight can easily be halted before a ship could reach the bar. Mergui is different; there is open water and ships waiting. Should the Siamese turn against us—and you can never tell—I can easily flee Mergui. Here, you are trapped.

A look of surprise crossed Phaulkon's face, but he said nothing.

"Do not think me a coward for talk of fleeing," White continued. "I am a realist. You have heard the extraordinary stories that are going around the bazaars, as I have, of you leading a possible rebellion. The Mandarins are suspicious of you and unhappy with the State of Affairs; you, a foreigner, so wealthy and powerful. I do not doubt you, nor your ability, but as we have just seen with the Makassars, the situation here is unstable. Nay, it's worse than that, it's explosive, Phaulkon. Should the King die, all hell will break loose." White paused and now reached for the brandy flask and filled his cup. He flushed with embarrassment. "My apologies. I should not let my tongue run away with me."

Phaulkon sat still and stared down at the table. He was neither angered nor shocked at his friend's outspokenness. Nothing White had said was unexpected, and while he could have used him well as his assistant, he realized such a role was not in his nature. "White does not lack courage, he lacks a sense of duty," he thought to himself. "He has ambition, only his ambition is the same as all the other Europeans, to profit as quickly as possible and return to Europe to live like a Lord. Well, I live like a Lord now; I am a Lord, and there is no country in Europe that I can call home. My Duty lies here."

Suddenly he felt very alone. Speaking aloud he turned to White and raised his cup. "I appreciate your sincerity, Sam. Here . . . a toast to you, my friend. May you prosper in Mergui."

"And you, Sir," White replied. "May you prosper as Lord Wicha-yen."

Ayutthaya
17th October, 1686

White returned to Mergui yesterday and we exchanged gifts; he presenting Lady Phaulkon with some rubies and other precious trinkets, and she in return proffering Chinese silk and porcelain, all of the finest quality. I could not, however, give him the parting gift he wished. At his request, I have greatly increased his powers in Mergui and arranged for a Dual Communication with official dispatches for the Royal Court and private letters to myself giving fuller accounts of matters in hand.

To his last wish, however, I could not agree. Ever desirous to cover himself, White had asked me for a letter stating that Coates' actions at Madapollam nearly a year previously had been officially sanctioned by the Siamese Court. I know that he wishes this to avoid any future accusations of piracy, but it is impossible for me to obtain such a letter, which would require lying to the King. White argued well for what he wanted, but I remained Resolute.

Why did I not agree? I am by no means certain myself. It is, of course, useful to have a hold over White should I need it one day. Though there is more than that. I do not trust him fully; I think his nerve is going. True, I have given more power to his position as Customs Master of Mergui, yet I am not certain what his plans are—to stay put or to cut and run with the fortune he has already amassed. It does not really matter, as I have high hopes the French will become a greater force in the Bay of Bengal. Much depends on how much of a commitment they are prepared to make. That I will know soon enough.

Also what the English East India Company might do is a question in my mind. Judging by George White's letters, I can perhaps, in the name of Narai, make an agreement with King James II directly, bypassing the Company. Maybe I am simply trying to keep all options open to me. But I am uneasy.

34

With White returned to Mergui and by all accounts making himself a very busy man, Phaulkon had time to undertake important business of his own, and set about composing a long and carefully considered letter to Père de la Chaise, advisor to King Louis XIV. He wished to reinforce what he had briefed Fr. Tachard to do on his return to France, and to confirm the situation that stood at the end of de Chaumont's visit, as well as to relate what had happened since the Ambassador's departure.

Firstly in the letter, he clarified the fact that the terms of the agreement which had been granted de Chaumont had not been made public—he never intended they would be—and gave some legitimacy as to why this should have been so. Accordingly, he informed the Rev. Fr. briefly of the Makassar Rebellion and pointed out that one could readily imagine how such an Innovation in Religious Matters as allowed in the agreement would have been seized upon by the rebels to justify their conduct, and what support it would have brought to their banners.

Phaulkon wrote that nonetheless the missionaries in Siam, who were not Jesuits, never gave him a moment's respite. "Fortunately," he added, "the Bishop of Metellopolis, is more moderate and only asks that the King utter a Fresh Confirmation of his willingness to support the aims of the Catholic Church in Siam, and so satisfy opinion in France.

His request startles me, seeing that he knows His Majesty's Intentions just as well as I do, having been present at all the Audiences granted to the Ambassador, when the King had confirmed these privileges more than once, and evinced his Delight in granting them out of consideration for His Most Christian King. To mention these matters again to King Narai would throw doubt on his sincerity and expose me to reproach from him."

The question of the King's Promise to acquaint himself with the mysteries of the Catholic Religion was also addressed. "In this matter," Phaulkon informed Père de la Chaise, "I have advised the Bishop to come to the Palace, and at an appropriate moment I report his arrival so that Narai might grant an Audience. His Majesty is always pleased to see the Bishop, but what he said to me after one Audience was such that I feel I should quote his actual words:

"'I should be only too glad,' Narai told me, 'to fulfill my promise to the Most Christian King. I often think of it, but what renders it almost beyond my power is my inability to understand the Bishop.'"

Phaulkon continued to say that he doubted if the Bishop's Audiences would produce any results so long as he limited himself to trying to explain the History of the Creation. "I can hardly blame the King for the difficulty he experienced in attempting to fathom such a complex theological point," the Greek reported. "I suggested, therefore, to the Bishop that something more practical, perhaps some extracts from books which contain clear references to God's Providence in preserving states, countries, and their inhabitants, might provide a more graspable message. To assist in this, I lent him a long account of the Siege of Vienna, wherein Divine Providence is Plainly Manifest in the salvation of the city; since the credit for it belongs neither to the city's defences nor to the Emperor's troops.

"A translation was made of this work but it, too, has failed to enlighten King Narai, and I am forced to admit the account was perhaps not expressed clearly enough for someone imperfectly acquainted with the State of Europe. I made a revision of the translation, however, and the King has shown much pleasure in reading it, and I have persuaded the Bishop to continue in these efforts, as well as advising him to improve his command of Siamese, especially the Language of Court, so that he may better communicate with His Majesty. As I explained to him, Saint Francis Xavier surely did not make conversions in this part of the East by merely talking of Heaven and Hell. It was not enough for Our Saviour to teach men of things appertaining to Heaven and the Trinity: he also expounded the parables of the sower and of the king who raised an army for the conquest of another land, which could only be done by Employing Words in General Use."

Phaulkon was careful in his letter to make it clear that his object in mentioning these matters was not to put blame on the Bishop. Rather he explained his purpose was to indicate to Père de la Chaise a Favourable Situation in Siam, and if all the benefits for the Faith which were desired in France were not immediately forthcoming, the fault would not rest with him.

To leave no doubt, he added: "There is no need for me to expatiate further upon the intentions of my Master. All I can say is that he has made them as clear to me as any king has the right to do to his Ministers, to whom the King's Will is generally made known by his actions rather than by word of mouth. His Most Christian Majesty will be able to construe my King's True Disposition from the manner in which he governs. I would not imply by this that it is his wish to become a Christian: I can only say that he directs his policy as though he aims to give satisfaction to His Most Christian Majesty."

In this way Phaulkon established—or so hoped he had done—that progress according to the Wishes of the King of France was being made in Siam, and that King Narai was, by his actions if not by his beliefs, conducting his reign in a manner that should prove favourable to the French.

To stress what he was seeking, Phaulkon explained that King Narai had instructed him to find Christians capable of officiating in the Government of his Provinces, his Garrisons, his Palace guards, and other important Civil and Military Functions. The reason for this being that the King could not trust his own subjects in the case of an outbreak.

It was crucial to Phaulkon's plans, essential, as he saw it, to the very success of Narai's Reign, that the French understood this, and not make the mistake, as he thought de Chaumont had, of trying to set sail before weighing anchor. Because of dissatisfaction among certain of the Mandarins and Buddhist clerics with the King's Protection of Foreigners, there was a danger that Narai would be forced to change his ideas to the Prejudice of the Christian Religion unless there was provision to fortify his position.

To achieve this aim, as Phaulkon explained to de la Chaise, he trusted his proposals sent via Fr. Tachard would receive a favourable response in France, and that some thirty good and qualified Christian men would be sent to Siam to assume positions of Provincial Governors and similar.

Already worried about how far he could trust Samuel White, the Greek emphasized the value and Exceptional Facilities of Mergui as a trading station, where he expressed a wish to see the civil, military, and maritime administration vested in the hands of some trusted servant of France acting, of course, in the name of the King of Siam, although he would hold disciplinary authority over them.

Phaulkon purposely omitted from the letter any mention of Singora. Although this port had been granted to the French in the agreement with de Chaumont, the Greek hoped that his praises of Mergui would cause the French to direct their efforts in that quarter, and thus effectively remove Samuel White who, Phaulkon believed was becoming a loose cannon, a Liability that he could not afford.

Phaulkon concluded his letter by apprising the Rev. Fr. of news of the East, of the activities of the Dutch and of the English, as well as of matters affecting Siam's Own Relations with its neighbours Vientiane and Cambodia.

Louvo
3rd March, 1687

My fears about Samuel White are confirmed by the reports I receive from my agents in Mergui. Far from being chastened by the Inquiry into his Activities, and my refusal to provide him letters that will exonerate him from any charges of acts of piracy that the English Company could possibly bring against him, he has returned to Mergui even more committed to his rapacious ways than before. I can only conclude that he is preparing to make a final haul of booty before fleeing to England.

Already he has sent out his two big ships, the *Resolution* and the *Revenge*, as well as the frigate *Dorothy* and several armed merchantmen, to prowl the Bay of Bengal and seize whatever comes their way.

All of this makes it clear to me that White has lost all Sense of Proportion and is Acting as a Despot. I hear that even his trusted secretary Davenport thinks him rash to the point of insanity. Hardly surprising when, as the latest reports tell me, he has had the Audacity to seize a piece of Burmese territory

He is now beyond my control, and to protect myself and Siam I can do no other than maintain an Official Stance. It is thus that I will write to him, demanding that he withdraw immediately from Burma, and in future be more cautious how he proceeds in such affairs without first advising the Siamese Court.

But what use is there in writing letters. Why, I warned him three months ago that intelligence received by the Siamese suggests the English Company at Madras is planning a strike against Mergui, and I advised White it would be prudent to send out no ships. He did not heed that advice and blithely wrote that he believes Madras would not break openly with Siam just now as it is occupied with operations in India.

Events have proved him wrong. News reaches me, and doubtless White also, that the English Company has been reinforced and plans to take Mergui. Now more than ever, my overtures to the French appear the correct, nay the only path for Siam, and we will be able to protect ourselves should the English seek reprisals against us for White's filibustering. White will be hanged as a pirate, but I will triumph. The Mandarins will have to accept my policy and see its justness.

White has chosen his own path against my advice and I cannot be accused of throwing him to the dogs of war. He is no fool for all his rashness and greed, and I am certain he will have made contingency to save his own skin.

35

Beneath a surface calm, Mergui was in a shambles. The several ships to be seen in the port and the stacks of cargo on the wharf gave the appearance of normalcy but belied a fear. European traders and seamen went briskly about their business as if in a hurry to be finished, and few lingered in conversation as they had before, enjoying a pipe of tobacco over the exchange of news. Wary glances replaced the easy air of the past, and white faces stood out from the crowds all the more for being shunned by the Siamese and the Mohammedan merchants.

Burnaby had proven a weak Governor, while Samuel White, the man ostensibly with the power of command, had lost control and had become unbearably authoritarian in an attempt to deny, as much to himself as to others, the situation in which he found himself, isolated and friendless with no support from Siam against the English, even less English protection should Siam turn against him, and Phaulkon, his champion, ready to disown him should his position be compromised.

In his desperation, White forged a document, complete with the seals and signature of two Siamese Mandarins, dated back to 1685, stating that he was subject to the Orders of Siam. He was nonetheless alone. The other English in Mergui avoided him, and finally even Davenport resigned his position, no longer able to tolerate the man's madness.

Yet White was not mad, if one discounted an Uncontrollable Lust for riches, for he had the presence of mind to load the *Dorothy* with all his amassed treasure and to provision her sufficiently to feed forty men for 18 months. This was to be his escape to England, where he trusted his forged document of authorization would clear him of any charges of piracy that the English might bring against him.

He could not, however, use any documents to hide his preparations to flee from the Siamese, and White's fitting out the *Dorothy* quickly aroused gossip. Rumours of his untimely departure became rife in the Mergui bazaars; nor was the talk dispelled when White flogged an Indian merchant whom he suspected of spreading suspicion.

By the middle of April, White had completed his preparations and planned to sail at the end of the month. But on the 23rd, the *Resolution*, which he feared had been lost, returned to port with news that the *Revenge* and another ship had been taken by the English East India Company, which was about to launch a direct assault on Mergui in reparation for losses inflicted upon it by the Siamese and by White.

Displaying remarkable presence of mind, White was not panicked into immediate flight, and instead risked delay in order to transfer all his wealth and supplies from the *Dorothy* to the *Resolution*, a much larger ship.

Events were to repeat themselves two months later, when news arriving in Mergui again halted White's departure, re-scheduled for the end of June. An English man-of-war lay outside the bar, White was told, and his hopes of flight vanished at the sight of the *Curtana*, a 24-gun frigate, blocking the exit of shipping out of the port. Word quickly reached him that the ship had been sent, under the command of a 29-year-old, Captain Anthony Weltden, by the English Company to deliver to him and Burnaby a Proclamation of King James II, charging them to leave the King of Siam's Service and proceed to Fort St. George.

All other English subjects in Mergui were also Commanded to Quit Siamese Employ. Weltden had further orders to take possession of all Siamese revenue in White's keeping as part settlement of claims for damages against the Company amounting to 65,000 pounds. The reparation, mostly arising from the activities of Captain Coates in the Bay of Bengal, was addressed to Phaulkon, who was viewed by the Company as having Mismanaged Siam's Affairs without the Knowledge of the King.

φ

"God! Is there no way out of this wretched hole?" White slumped in his chair, his hands flung up to cover his face. Suddenly he leapt up and grabbed the English sailor who had reported to him the presence of the *Curtana*. "Quick, man," he commanded. "Take what men you need and set up a shore battery with a line of fire across the harbour. Hurry!"

"Sir, with respect, it be too late," the sailor replied. "That *Curtana* will be in port afore we've time to move a cannon. Tide's already turned."

White considered. "Aye. You're right. Well, my friend, when you can't fight, you use diplomacy. Gather a reception party and join me at the harbour. The Company deserves a fitting welcome."

White's spirits had revived. He was a pragmatic man, and as soon as he saw that resistance was impossible, he became resigned to talking himself out of trouble.

Two hours later, he presented himself at the wharf, where a surly bunch of ill-disciplined sailors had been drawn up into something approximating a welcoming committee, some of them even remembering to salute when the Captain of the *Curtana* came ashore.

"Samuel White, Sir, *Shahbandar* of Mergui," announced White to the youthful master who stepped onto the wharf.

"Ah, yes, I was informed. My name is Weltden, Anthony Weltden, Captain of the Company ship *Curtana*. It is my duty . . ."

"Welcome to Mergui, Captain. An honour indeed. Come, you must be tired after the passage from Madras. Please allow me to offer refreshments. My house is not far. Burnaby also awaits you there." White spoke quickly, taking the wind from Weltden's sails.

Young, impressionable, and lacking in guile—and so incapable of recognizing it in others—Weltden accepted White's hospitality. He returned with him to his house, where he met Burnaby and the English merchants, all of whom willingly submitted to his authority.

Cordial relations were soon established. White promised Weltden that he would comply with his instructions, and invited him to stay at his house, where the Captain was told he would find the nights cooler than on his ship.

ф

Days passed without Weltden taking any action against White, with whom he was charged to bring back to Madras. He may have fooled himself that he was playing a cat-and-mouse game with White until he had had time to fully appraise the situation and consider his tactics. But he was untutored in the ways of the East, and was angered when Davenport, now turned against his former employer, warned him of White's duplicity.

"I have promised Mister White and Mister White has promised me so fairly that I do much doubt being overreached by him," Weltden told Davenport, who was astounded at the man's naïvety.

Having granted the Siamese a sixty-day armistice in order to ensure calm—though, with only a small force at his command, Weltden had never fully considered his actions should he meet with resistance after that time—the Captain allowed himself to be lulled into inactivity by White's charm and their mutual fondness for English ale. He did take the precaution of securing the *Resolution* and mooring her close to the *Curtana*, but otherwise he discounted rumours variously of White's planned armed resitance and his Proposed Flight. Mostly he gave himself up to a succession of drinking bouts either at White's house or aboard the *Curtana*, where casks of ale flowed freely and cannon were fired simply for the jest of it.

With the would-be captor and his captive carousing, the local Mandarins took the opportunity to re-appraise their situation. There were five Siamese who, along with Burnaby and White, comprised the Council that governed Mergui, and which was directly responsible to the Siamese Court at Ayutthaya.

None of these five Mandarins had previously attempted to interfere with White's activities; they may have sympathized and lent their tacit support to local protests by the Mohammedans, but they never openly opposed the English, justifying their negligence by assuming that because White and Burnaby were appointees of Phaulkon, it was not their place to ask questions.

Now, confronted by the *Curtana*, an armed foreign vessel riding high in the harbour, and its Captain, an Englishman, ordering reparations, their situation had changed. They were not concerned with White's predicament, nor especially with the damages demanded, but what they did fear was that White would trade Mergui to the English Company in exchange for any charges against him being dropped. With Weltden already there and the *Curtana* blocking his escape, it was all he had to bargain with.

Convinced they needed to act quickly, the Mandarins took matters into their own hands without consulting Ayutthaya, and plotted a pre-emptive strike. Ill-feeling against White had long been rife among the local population, and the Mandarins had no difficulty rounding up a mob keen for English blood.

φ

White accompanied Weltden to the dock after an evening
drinking onshore. "Who's there?" he called out, peering into the
darkness. Thick monsoon cloud obscured the moon and he could
see nothing.

"What is it, man? Not like you to be jittery. There's no one there."
Weltden turned and walked towards the wharf to be ferried out to
his ship. He heard nothing save the slapping of the water against
the piles of the wharf.

Suddenly the quiet was rent by screams, and a blow knocked
him unconscious.

White had only a moment to glimpse an armed band of Siamese
and Burmese breaking out of the darkness before his servant pulled
him back into the shadows and the gang rushed past unseeing.

Confused by the suddenness of the attack, White first made
steps towards home. He then heard more yells from the darkness
around him, and realized that the assault on Weltden had not been
an isolated one. The whole town sounded as if it was under attack.
Near the gate of his house he saw a wild mob, and knew now that
Mergui was in the grip of some uprising. His only hope of survival
was to reach the *Resolution*. He ran back to the harbour and jumped
aboard Weltden's barge and cast off.

Weltden had by now recovered consciousness and dragged himself to hide in the shallows. By great good fortune, the moon shone
through a break in the clouds as White rowed past. He spotted the
injured Captain and hauled him out of the water. Floundering in
the black of the night, the two eventually reached the *Resolution* and
the *Curtana*, and took both ships out of the bay to find shelter
among the islands.

Mergui town was in chaos. The normal night-time calm was
shattered by cannon fire, the yells of angry mobs, the screams of
their victims, and the pounding of the feet of those desperately
trying to flee.

φ

By dawn, a sort of peace had returned, but over sixty Englishmen had been slaughtered, including Richard Burnaby, who was cut down in his own home. The rest of the English population, along with the women and children were spared.

From his ship, White stared at the town, wisps of smoke slowly breaking up in the still morning air. Then, looking down, he saw the bodies of five Englishmen washed out from the shore by the tide, each one horribly mutilated in death.

Ayutthaya
21st August, 1687

The English at Mergui have been massacred and the French
are shortly to arrive. I cannot yet tell to what extent the Mandarins
were behind the slaughter, which I view as much as an Indirect
Attack against me as a Direct Assault on White. In manipulating
news of the affair, I make every effort to play it down and state that
the deaths were caused by the mob running Amok and not due to
a planned action with the Sanction of the Siamese Court.

After learning of Weltden's arrival in Mergui, I did take the precaution to publish on behalf of Siam a Declaration of War against
the English East India Company, though not against England herself. I want there to be no doubt that any appearance of hostility
on my part is in Response to Provocation and not initiated by me.
I am a man of peace, of moderation.

36

The second French Embassy to grace the Shores of Siam in as many years arrived at the bar of the river below Bangkok on 27th September, 1687. It was a grand and imposing expedition of six ships, including two men-of-war, with 636 soldiers and officers under the command of General Desfarges, an elderly military man.

In charge of the Mission were two Plenipotentiary Envoys from Louis XIV, with whom Phaulkon would have to negotiate. The first of these, a man older than the Greek, was Claude Cébéret, a Director of the French Company and to all appearances an honest and passive man. It was his duty to take responsibility for matters of trade.

The other Envoy, also Phaulkon's senior in years, was a different proposition. Simon de la Loubère, a barrister by profession, though with some diplomatic experience, carried a reputation both as an intellectual—mathematician, philologist, and composer of light verse—and as a haughty, irritable man who did not easily win the sympathy of his fellow men. De la Loubère had been instructed to oversee political and religious affairs.

A more friendly face from Phaulkon's point of view was that of Fr. Tachard, who was accompanying Siam's Own Returning Ambassador, Kosa Pan, together with 14 Jesuits. Completing the party were the Abbé de Lionne and several missionaries.

Although Tachard was a member of the Mission, he also acted as Phaulkon's private secretary in his dealings with France. In order to apprise his master of the situation and so arrange matters between themselves before any meeting, he had arrived at Ayutthaya in advance of the Mission, having taken separate passage from Batavia, where all the ships had made their first landfall in the East Indies.

φ

"That cannot be true. All troops in Bangkok and Mergui. . . ? None in Singora?" Phaulkon questioned Tachard after his arrival at Ayutthaya.

"Those are the Instructions from King Louis XIV which the Envoys will present to you," Tachard replied. "This is a copy of King Louis' Letter. It says: 'It is His Majesty's Pleasure that Father Tachard be deputed to make the following proposal to Lord Constant—namely, that the King of Siam authorizes the appointment of a French Governor at Bangkok, who shall be responsible to himself; also that he admits a French garrison to this town, and permits . . .'"

"No, no, a thousand times no," Phaulkon interrupted. "Any French Provincial Governors must be under my direct control. That was in my letter to Père de la Chaise. What else?"

"The instructions also call for a garrison and a Governor at Mergui, which is viewed as essential for the Trade of Siam in the Bay of Bengal, as is Bangkok for that of the Gulf and onward China Trade. . . .

"And, listen to this, my dear Constance, there are also Secret Instructions saying: 'There is no indication that the Envoys will encounter any difficulty in regard to these matters which they will make on His Siamese Majesty. Moreover, nothing could be worse than to have to apply pressure, since it would Gravely Prejudice the cause of Christianity, and would complicate the task of the trading Company. Nevertheless, if any change should have occurred in the Sentiments of the King during the period that has elapsed since Father Tachard left Siam, and if no hope remains of negotiating with success, in that event His Majesty is determined to force an entry into Bangkok . . . etcetera, etcetera. . . .'

"Finally, Phaulkon, the instructions say you are to be brought into the French confidence, and to be honoured with the title of Count and awarded the Order of Saint Michel."

"Count. . . ? The Order of Saint Michel. . . ? Well, that indeed gladdens me. However, Père de la Chaise has responded only too well to my letter. I did suggest the importance of Mergui, though I never expected such a Blatant Demand. Nor did I call for 600 troops. I wanted fifty or sixty good Frenchmen to take strategic posts. . . .

"Well, so be it. Now . . . Kosa Pan: I pray that he is in no way privy to the True Purpose of the troops. For my part, in so far as I have made anything public, a French garrison is intended only for Singora, in the South, as a deterrent against the Dutch, according to my agreement two years ago with de Chaumont."

"But of course, Constance," Tachard answered. "Kosa Pan knows nothing of these arrangements."

"Good. Then my problem now is to persuade the Siamese of the Desirability of such a plan. At least the initiative lies with me to arrange matters without Kosa Pan's interference. . . . Father, I am truly proud that France is to bestow upon me the Rank of Count and the Order of Saint Michel. It is a Gesture of Gratitude that I duly respect, but I am sorely Angered and Alarmed by the rest of King Louis' Instructions to his Envoys. But that I must deal with. . . .

"I thank you for your loyalty. Now I bid you go greet the Envoys and give them my assurance that I will see that a reception be prepared for them as grand as that which we accorded de Chaumont."

Ayutthaya
1st October, 1687

I have kept much to myself these past few days, pondering in solitude how I may best settle matters with the French. I could not bring myself to tell Maria of my anger and my fears. They would only alarm her and she would plead again for us to leave Siam before I lose everything. That was one good thing Fr. Tachard had told me: I have been given the right of residence in France. Still, I cannot leave now, not without seeing my plans through.

I am alone. There is no one, save Maria, I can trust, and therefore no one to whom I can speak honestly. I dearly wish I could have persuaded Samuel White to have joined as my assistant so that I might have had someone to share my burden, but he was either too fearful or too anxious to safeguard his riches. Lady Phaulkon is of course my Greatest Support, and I can trust her with my life, but I own to a feeling of guilt in putting her in danger by insisting we remain in Siam. There is nothing I can do; dearly though I love her, I am powerless to change what Fate may will.

So I have struggled as to how I can satisfy the French and still keep the Initiative. I sat here at my desk and my head reeled. I toyed with the paper, quills, and ink, aligning them then re-arranging them again as I weighed in my mind one idea against another.

Three score good Frenchman to serve as administrators is what I had wanted. Instead, 600 soldiers to be quartered in Bangkok and Mergui, not distant Singora. It is too much. Tachard at least must know such an action will strain my position as Narai's Favourite, my one true source of strength, as well as make me extremely un-popular with the Mandarins, who will topple me if I lose Narai's Trust. Yet what am I to do? If I refuse King Louis I will lose the French support that I need to maintain my power, even more so since I have Declared War on the English Company. If I agree to the terms in their entirety, it is possible I will lay myself open to a charge of Treason against Siam.

Finally, I have come upon a solution and have written a letter to Tachard, not only to communicate the thoughts I have arrived at, but also to clarify those same ideas in my own mind. I wrote in Portuguese, the language we habitually converse in, and deliberately chose a pompous tone to convey my pique at apparently being so little trusted that I had to deal with new French Envoys.

I began with King Louis' Instructions as I see them, namely that in order to ensure the safety of the Christian Community in Siam, the fort at Bangkok is to be made more effective with King Narai's Permission, and manned by a garrison of French soldiers who are to be placed at King Narai's Disposal. Moreover, in order to further trade between France and Siam, Mergui should be similarly garri-soned so as to afford the protection of French traders in the event of hostilities on behalf of the Dutch.

I did not question King Louis' Demands, which in many respects are similar to my own proposal, with the exception that I do not wish for such a large contingent of French troops and, more importantly, I must have authority over the foreigners. What I did stress to Tachard was that if I do advise Narai to allow foreigners to occupy his fortresses, I may be accused of Breaking my Allegiance to him, and that is something I am incapable of doing even to gain thereby the whole world.

A dilemma has been thrust upon me and threatens to ruin my plans. Still, I am certain of the Destiny that has brought me from the poverty of my birthplace to be the Trusted Favourite of the King of Siam, a man who, in his Kindness and Graciousness, is to me more a father than a master. I believe that I can never be accused of treason so long as I remain True to my God and my King.

So in my letter to Tachard I agree to all of King Louis' Requests and promise to obtain Full Assent from our King. In return, I will require that the French troops swear an Oath of Allegiance to the King of Siam, and that the only orders they are to obey will be those issued by me.

This letter will amount to a Treaty between Siam and France. I made a few other not unreasonable stipulations: officers, other than the French, should be appointed only by myself; all plans and specifications for the construction of fortresses must be approved by me; rewards, promotions, and punishments regarding both soldiers and officers will require my Prior Sanction. Finally I insisted on a clause whereby the Treaty, as agreed between myself and Fr. Tachard, and as conveyed to the two Envoys, will not be published nor communicated by the Written Word or by Word of Mouth to anyone except the King of France.

It is far from ideal, but is possible, and allows ways for my schemes to progress. But there is always Human Fallibility. Why, oh why, has France had to send two Envoys? All could have been conducted between myself and the worthy Fr. Tachard. I have been directing Siamese Trade for five years—always in accordance with my King's Wishes—alone. Are the fruits of it all to be plucked untimely before fully ripened, all because of Petty Animosities? The English can never set a proper course, and now I fear the French, on whom I pin my hopes, are in danger of similar Disunity of Purpose and Command.

37

Fr. Tachard had journeyed from Bangkok to Ayutthaya to inform Phaulkon of the latest information he had gleaned after welcoming the French Mission on its arrival in the Menam River.

"Constance, I have important news that you must know before you meet our Envoys. It will give an advantage in your negotiations. I think I am safe in saying that you may discount the threat in King Louis' Letter of imposing force on Bangkok should diplomacy fail. As we all know, the taking of the town would be perilous, and would depend entirely on General Desfarges. He, thank God, has now seen the reality of the situation and, supported by my arguments, has told the Envoys that while he is prepared to die fighting for the Glory of France, he has lost one-third of his troops on the voyage out, and the rest are weakened and in no fit state to fight. And so the Envoys are left with no viable alternative than to accept the proposals of your draft Treaty. The threat of force can be discounted."

"Father, I am greatly relieved at the report you bring," Phaulkon said. "It seems, from what you say, that this Desfarges is a practical man like myself. A potential ally, yes?"

"It would seem so. And, with respect, it is an ally that you will need," Tachard said, his eyes wide in a knowing expression.

Phaulkon was again alarmed. "Why so, particularly. What do you mean?"

"I have heard that that idiot Monsieur Véret, manager of the French Company here, visited la Loubère and Cébéret on board their ship with the sole purpose of slandering you. He told the Envoys that Chevalier de Forbin's good name was ruined by you and that he was forced to leave Siam because of your jealousy of him. I know the truth is that he misjudged the Makassars and failed in his command in Bangkok, almost getting himself killed in the process, but lies and half-truths spill from Véret's mouth, poisoning the minds of the Envoys and turning them against you, saying how overbearing you are."

"So, Véret accuses me of being overbearing, does he?" Phaulkon looked amused. "Well, that would depend on the character of those with whom I must deal. I never suffer fools gladly, nor the pompous, nor the arrogant who would look down on a Greek. It is not I who is overbearing, rather it is I who am Borne Down Upon by others seeking their own Selfish Ends.

"Be that as it may, the loose talk of Véret and others does nothing to help the agreeable Acceptance of My Proposals, difficult enough in themselves. It worsens an already bad atmosphere and increases the doubts la Loubère and Cébéret must be now harbouring about the success of their Mission. You and I, Father, knowing the situation here, make Realistic Proposals that conform with the Wishes of Louis, but the Envoys, I fear, will see them as an attempt by me to turn French troops into Mercenaries of Siam."

Phaulkon paused and thought for a moment before speaking again, talking as much to satisfy himself as to ensure Tachard understood the matter.

"Father," he said, "while there is doubtless much argument among the members of the French Mission, their choices are limited. I am trying to make the best of it; I do not like the terms which the French present, but still I have returned with proposals that offer a compromise. I worry more about how my role will be viewed by the Siamese than about what decision la Loubère and Cébéret will come to. What options do they have? Only three that I can see: leave Siam immediately without having accomplished anything; take Bangkok by force; or accept the Treaty as I have outlined. To my mind, the first of these is pointless, and only the second and third options are worthy of consideration."

Bangkok
19th October, 1687

Glory shone down upon us yesterday. The annual rains have finished, and under a cloudless sky Desfarges landed his troops at Bangkok. The bright sunshine imbued the scene with brilliance and helped masked the pasty faces and weakened bodies of the soldiers who had suffered sorely from their long voyage and the days of idleness on board ship as they awaited orders. Sadly, King Narai is too ill, his health having deteriorated of late, to come to Bangkok to receive the Oath of Allegiance from the French, though the Mandarins in their golden-spired hats and the masses created a Fitting Sense of the Ceremonial.

In the absence of His Majesty it fell to me to receive the Oath. It was a proud moment, and I was amused to see looks of dour acceptance on the faces of la Loubère and Cébéret. They could scarcely hide a feeling of humiliation.

La Loubère's eyes and ears were constantly alert, hawk-like, inspecting all that went on about him. He appears to have an interest in Siam to a degree I have never before witnessed in any other foreigner. It was as if he were making an Inventory to get the measure of us. He was aloof, but did not miss much, and he asked many questions—why were the boats shaped thus; what did the Mandarins hats signify; why and how was this and that? Unceasing questions.

Though the swearing of the Oath of Allegiance was a moment of triumph for me, I realize I have won no new allies, with perhaps the exception of Desfarges. The Envoys, the French Company's Agent, and the non-Jesuit missionaries are all in opposition to me, not, I feel justified in saying, for any practical or logical reasons, but through Jealously of my Power and Position, or of a perceived sense of slight against their own self respect because they must negotiate through me, a low-born Greek.

The Siamese Mandarins are opposed to me for similar reasons. They seem incapable of accepting or even understanding that a foreigner might serve their own best interests. Only Narai shares my vision of what we might achieve to enhance Siam's Greatness.

I endure the opposition with which I have to contend daily. Yet I progress. The ceremony of the swearing of the Oath of Allegiance was glorious, and all praise me for the Grandeur of the Occasion.

38

After la Loubère and Cébéret had been duly welcomed at Bangkok, Phaulkon arranged for their transportation to Ayutthaya, where they were to be granted a Royal Audience. The two Envoys had heard of the ceremony with which de Chaumont had been received in 1685, thus Phaulkon had arranged a similarly magnificent fleet of barges to transport the Ambassadors upriver, together with the accompaniment of pipes and drums, the music of which, Cébéret later complained, fell harshly on the ears.

Phaulkon remained in Bangkok with General Desfarges to inspect the fortifications of the city, there being two forts under construction, one on each bank of the river.

"It will take a minimum of 1,200 men to defend those two positions, unless they are scaled down," Desfarges told Phaulkon after they had returned from their inspection and were taking refreshments in a tent that had been erected on the riverbank.

"Quite possibly, General," Phaulkon replied. "I bow to your military judgement. However, the Siamese, I fear, will not agree to a reduction in scale to correspond with the numbers of the troops. Appearance is everything in the East, and a reduction in size will be seen as a lack of commitment at best and disrespect at worst."

"Ground is no good either. Too swampy. Water's bad. Must be mosquitoes, too, I reckon," Desfarges said in his bluff manner that betold of a lifetime's soldiering which knew only of valour and not other qualities that would have allowed an appreciation of politics.

"Alas, General, it is, but the whole area is the same. Nothing can be done."

Desfarges sighed, resigned to the situation. Phaulkon warmed to the man, whom appeared to have a practical turn and would accept compromises and limitations.

Before their departure for Ayutthaya, the Envoys ordered that a detachment of troops should in time be sent to Mergui. Phaulkon protested strongly and was vociferously supported by Desfarges who was aware, as was the Greek, of the peril of dividing the French forces. But in this the Envoys could not be moved, and a precious 120 men were to be dispatched to the port.

"We'll have to make the best of it," Desfarges remarked about fortifying Bangkok with insufficient men. "Let's just pray to God that we'll not have to defend against any concerted attack."

"I'm afraid, General, our position is even weaker than you imagine," Phaulkon remarked quietly. "I will require about 35 men and their officers to be drafted into the ships that are to be stationed in the Gulf to combat pirate activities. What's more, I must have a bodyguard for King Narai at Louvo. That will leave you only 200 men to garrison Bangkok. Indeed, as you say, General, let us pray."

Ayutthaya
27th October, 1687

Am I never to be rid of these wretched Frenchmen? Just previously I had to postpone the Audience with the King because I was told some of the Royal Gifts brought by the Envoys had been damaged in transit and would have to be repaired. Now, having arranged for la Loubère and Céberét to be brought to the Capital in Grand Style, I found myself drawn into an argument over protocol. They had called at my house, to which I welcomed them cordially enough, serving refreshments and asking after their wellbeing. I then broached the subject of the ceremonial and honours that were to be accorded them at the forthcoming Royal Audience, and la Loubère complained at length telling me how, according to the custom in Europe, an Envoy expected equal or greater honours than an Ambassador. As an example, he mentioned some Marshal d'Humières who had been sent as an Envoy to England.

I insisted that regardless of what might be done in Europe, we in Siam consider an Ambassador to be of a Higher Rank than an Envoy. Thus, as these two Frenchmen were only Envoys, I explained that they were not entitled to those honours usually accorded Ambassadors.

"Envoys Extraordinary!" la Loubère almost shouted at me. "We, Phaulkon, are Envoys Extraordinary and you only need look at the practices of any of the Courts in Europe to see the precedents for the higher honours that are our due."

In causing la Loubère to lose his temper and raise his voice, I achieved my objective, namely to test if he is as quick-tempered as Tachard has warned me. I then abruptly let the matter drop.

"Come, I am about to dine," I said to them. "Pray, join me." It was not the most courteous of invitations. Yet the gesture reinforced my position over la Loubère and Céberet.

Tachard and the French officers joined us, but I did not ask Lady Phaulkon to grace us with her presence. As always, I prided myself on my lavish table, and on my wines, which were the best of several different lands. I made conversation about de Chaumont and how he was determined on one objective only, that of the conversion of Narai, when Tachard kicked me under the table. I took the hint and changed the topic. Tachard was correct and there was nothing to be gained by antagonizing these Envoys further. Shortly after the meal was finished, they departed.

39

On 2nd November, 1687, la Loubère and CéBéret attended their Audience with the King. The cannon fired a salute as the Envoys set out, and when they arrived at the Palace they walked between two rows of Mandarins in full dress uniform, who knelt and bowed their heads as the French passed. The ceremony was similar to that which I had arranged for de Chaumont, but this time there was no suspense when la Loubère gracefully presented the Royal Letter to King Narai.

All passed off in a most satisfactory fashion, except afterwards Cébéret complained of some of the arrangements:

"Why, Monsieur Phaulkon, were the umbrellas taken away when we reached the Palace," he said. "I had to walk through all those courtyards hatless under the blazing sun. I am sure I have caught a fever."

"My dear Cébéret," Phaulkon replied. "I am pained to hear you were inconvenienced. Please understand that it is the custom, and all procedures we follow are in Accordance with Siamese Tradition. It was the same when de Chaumont was received by His Majesty."

"If you say so, Sir. I have no way of judging otherwise. Nonetheless, I do not feel well and I am afraid that to my great regret I shall have to absent myself from the banquet tonight."

Cébéret retired with defiant poise that did not fully mask his hurt.

Was it an oversight that Phaulkon did not have the umbrellas kept for the walk to the Audience Hall? There were so many details to attend to in these affairs that he could have been excused for not thinking of everything.

φ

At the banquet that evening, there were no complaints from the French, perhaps because Cébéret was not present. Two thousand lamps, each within its own niche, flickered from the walls of the Palace courtyards as dish after lavish dish, both European and Siamese, were presented to the guests seated at tables decorated with fruit and vegetables carved in Exquisite Fashion into floral displays. Servants in red and gold livery poured the finest wines and liquors into cups of gold, while Siamese music sounded softly in the still night air. Beautiful young Siamese girls transformed the banquet into a Spectacle, dancing with a sinuous grace amid a blaze of stars as the light caught the coloured sequins and golden threads of their costumes.

The banquet rekindled Phaulkon's sense of hospitality and he forgot his differences with the French Envoys that threatened to keep them forever apart.

Ayutthaya
7th November, 1687

In the days following the Envoy's Audience with Narai, I had two Siamese assigned to escort la Loubère and Cébéret so that they might fully appreciate the Architectural Genius of the Royal Palace and the Buddhist temples that are the Glory of Ayutthaya.

I accompanied them on part of the tour, and took them by boat across the river to Wat Chai Wattanaram, one of my favourite temples in the city. It is of no great age, having been constructed only some fifty years ago, but is possessed of considerable charm. It has been built in like style to the great Angkor Wat in Cambodia, but modified somewhat to give the appearance of the polygonal chedis of the northern Lanna Kingdom. The square central courtyard, enclosed by brick walls and, at intervals, by secondary chambers with seven-tiered roofs, is dominated by a towering prang in the Khmer Style. Along the gallery is a row of Buddha images sat in silent meditation, heeding only the truth of the Dharma. The grassy slope in front of the temple is a restful spot where the townsfolk like to stroll, and I only regret it is not the kite-flying season, for in February and March the sky above Wat Chai is filled with flutterring creations of bamboo and paper like huge fabulous butterflies in all the hues of the rainbow.

It was a happy interlude for me, so rarely do I have the leisure to appreciate the beauty of the city I have come to love, second only in my affections to Louvo, which is to my mind more charming, if less beautiful, and more truly where power lies, just as is Versailles to Paris.

Alas, it was only an interlude, and problems mount upon me by the moment. I have ordered that Desfarges' men be issued with tents and mattresses. Even so, many of the soldiers, already weakened by the voyage from Europe, have fallen victim to fevers and bowel complaints, and this and the overall poor conditions of their billet have contributed towards a Disastrous Lack of Discipline among them. Regrettably, the General must divide his attention and is often absent from his men as I need him at Court to assist me in arranging the final terms of the Treaty.

At the same time, the spectre of the Mergui Massacre still haunts me, and the English, albeit from a distance, pose more trouble for me. They were alerted even before news of the massacre had spread abroad, and acted with alarm on learning earlier in the year that the French had dispatched a garrison to Siam. Their response was to plan to turn what had been a Punitive Expedition to Mergui, under Weldten, into a conquest, and so ordered the frigate *Pearl*, commanded by Captain James Perriman, to sail from Madras.

When, last 22nd September, the *Pearl* reached Mergui, she was challenged by a ship under Captain Cropley flying Siamese colours. Cropley refused to surrender and the *Pearl* gave chase—right into Mergui harbour where the luckless Perriman found himself surrounded by Siamese ships and he was the one to surrender—to a Frenchman, named Beauregard, whom I had managed to have replace the roles of White and Burnaby after the massacre. The two Company representatives aboard the *Pearl*, William Hodges and

John Hill, were taken prisoner and sent to Ayutthaya where I had them gaoled. Though with the French Embassy arrived, I quickly saw other uses for them, and they were recently released.

It was my intention that Hodges and Hill be allowed to return to Madras so that the True Facts concerning the Mergui Massacre should be learned by the Company from one of its own agents. It was thus reported by Hodges that although an armistice was in force, Weltden had breeched it by firing a salvo from the *Curtana*, thus provoking the attack on himself. This was essentially true; the fact the cannon had been fired in a drunken revelry and not out of hostility was irrelevant, the Mandarins arguing they were not to know it was not an intentional Act of Aggression. Hodges also reported that, as I had made clear, the regrettable loss of life was not authorized, the killing being the work of an Uncontrollable Mob.

A Declaration of War on behalf of Siam against the English Company, not England, seems to me reasonable, certainly as I do not discount the risk of England declaring war on us.

It is a constant juggle. Though I fancy I have all in hand.

40

In an impassioned speech lasting more than ninety minutes, the man who was Phaulkon's greatest enemy, the man who had always feigned indifference to Court Affairs, had argued against giving the French the strongholds that they asked for in Bangkok and Mergui, going so far as to give the King a history lesson in the fates of other earlier Eastern rulers who had admitted European troops, whether they were Portuguese or the Dutch, into their lands only to find themselves reduced to little better than Slavery.

"Behead me; my life is forfeit by reason of my defiance. But never will I give my consent to a Policy so Fatal to the Interest of Your Majesty," Phra Petracha declared in the King's Council.

"We believe in your sincerity, Phra Petracha," King Narai replied after the man had concluded his speech with those final words of defiance. "We also believe your unfortunate outburst was spontaneous, caused by your profound sense of loyalty to Us, and so we excuse it. We consider, however, your warnings about the French to be unfounded. We favour the arguments of Monsieur Phaulkon, who has shown admirable understanding in the furtherance of Our Ideas toward other Nations."

Petracha could do nothing but bow to the King and keep his silence, while in his heart hatred welled up against Phaulkon. He had repeatedly said in Council that he remained at Court solely out of personal interest for the King and would otherwise have entered the monkhood, a suggestion he effected by often wearing yellow dress so near the colour of the Buddhist robes. In truth, his outburst had been prompted by his fears over the size of the French force that had come to Siam, which was far greater than he had expected and would shift the balance in Phaulkon's favour should he oppose the Greek.

But Phaulkon had prepared his ground well, and before the Council met, he had taken every opportunity to remind Narai of the menace to Bangkok posed by Dutch hostility, and to Mergui by the English.

In this the King was satisfied. Nor was Petracha's distrust of the French supported by the people of Bangkok and Mergui, who themselves had long-held fears about the Dutch and the English.

Having failed to win over the King, and seeing that he lacked allies among the ordinary people, Petracha moved to appeal to their superstitious minds, and ordered one of the Brahmin astrologers make public that the stars ordained the French would at first be welcomed with open arms, and then their demands would be their undoing, causing a Great Upheaval in the course of which they would be Expelled from the Land with great loss of life among themselves and their supporters.

Louvo
18th November, 1687

La Loubère and Cébéret have accepted a Royal Invitation to visit Louvo, and I so arranged their journey that they arrived by night at this enchanting city, equally the favourite of mine as of His Majesty's as a respite when the intrigues of Ayutthaya become overbearing.

A long procession of torch bearers heralded our guests' arrival. Greeted by the city's Governor and senior Mandarins, they were taken to the grand brick house close by my own, where they were lodged with considerable luxury in spacious rooms provided with rich Chinese furnishings. The chapel in the grounds of my own house at Louvo has just been completed, and to mark the occasion, a Mass was held in the French Manner, to which our guests were pleased to attend, along with Lady Phaulkon, who impressed the French with her quiet piety that gives the lie to her pagan beauty.

It seems that my plans could reach fruition; the Treaty with the French will be signed, and if the Mandarins make no issue and allow sufficient time for the French troops to recover from their ailments, our position will be consolidated, regardless of what the English or Dutch might do, or what conspiracy Petracha may devise.

At ease with matters, last night I invited la Loubère and Céberet to dine at my house. It was the grandest of banquets, with European hors d'oevres and an eight-course Chinese dinner. There were performances of Siamese opera, Thai dance drama, and a puppet show, as well as a display of fireworks that the Orientals make so much more spectacular than anyone else. The French were thrilled, judging the fun of the evening by how much of my crystal was broken, and predicted a long and close friendship between us.

41

An ill temper consumed Phaulkon in spite of the success of his entertainments for the French at Louvo, and when la Loubère and Cébéret came to him the following afternoon, he rounded on them and raised a subject that had thus far been skirted by all.

"You know well that King Narai has not yet become a Catholic," Phaulkon yelled. "And why? Because he has not received sufficient instruction. The Bishop of Metellopolis has been in Siam for more than twenty years, yet he still cannot speak the language properly. How can the King learn if he cannot understand what is being taught to him? What is it you people expect? Am I to do everything myself?"

Disbelief and shock showed on the faces of the Envoys. "Sir, replied Cébéret, "this is a weighty matter. We must have time to consult among ourselves."

After the two Frenchmen had hurried from Phaulkon's house, Maria asked her husband why he had made such an Uncivil Outburst.

"My dear," he answered, "do you not see, my anger is but feigned, have no fear. It is not a question of Narai's conversion—you know my position on that—it is pure madness even to contemplate it. No, the reality is that my supporters among the French are the Jesuits, and so if I can sow seeds of doubt about the Bishop, call into question his credibility, the more authority I have on my side. This whole question of Narai's conversion, which that fool de Chaumont made so much of, could have destroyed me, the King, and the ideas we pursue. That is why I never made public any of the negotiations or agreements with de Chaumont. It is nothing to do with religion, but everything to do with politics."

"Oh, Constantine, dear Constantine," Maria said. "When will you ever stop plotting and scheming. This is no more your country than it is mine."

"Ah, my love. You are right in that. But this is where Fate has led me and where I must act out whatever is the Divine Plan that has brought me so far. I know it is hard on you. Do I ask too much of you. . . ? Say so, if that is what you truly think."

"No, no, a thousand times no. This is your Path and I, as your wife must follow. I support you with all my strength. I just beg that you be careful."

"Have no fear, I will. Now let us await what our dear Bishop will say to the Envoys."

Louvo
27th November, 1687

Father Laneau, Bishop of Metellopolis, has been questioned by la Loubère and Cébéret, and denies that the King's lack of learning in the Christian Faith is in any way due to his own shortcomings, and that he speaks Siamese perfectly well. Far from accepting any responsibility, he accuses me of hindering efforts at His Majesty's conversion, adding that the Concession purported to be given the Christians to build churches is in fact no Concession at all, since Mohammedans and Chinese enjoy a similar favour and are allowed to build their mosques and temples in Siam.

The latter is quite true, but the Bishop is wrong when he suggests I am afraid that if he converts Narai then I will lose Royal Patronage and he would become His Majesty's Favourite. Hearing this from Tachard, I burst out laughing at the thought of that ignorant Bishop supplanting me.

Tachard is a faithful servant and he argues vehemently in my defence during these discussions that the French have among themselves. Their disagreements serve my purpose well, and I am certain that rumours of it will be reported to the Mandarins, who will see that I am not attempting to undermine the King's Adherence to Buddhism. At the same time, my good works in extending Assistance to the Christians in Siam, albeit falling well short of actually trying to spread the Religion, along with the many charitable works of Lady Phaulkon, who cares for a large number of orphaned boys and girls, protect me from any charge the French might claim that I am an Enemy of Christianity.

I must own, however, yesterday was a testing time when the Envoys had a Second Audience with Narai, and la Loubère insisted I translate to His Majesty that King Louis' Principal Aim in the commerce of the Indies is the advancement of the Christian Religion. What I actually translated was that the French, unlike the Dutch and the Spanish, have no designs on capturing any country and rely solely on the Protection of Notre Dame de Lorette.

Narai listened then rose without saying anything, indicating the Audience was ended. There was an embarrassed silence when we were left alone, and I told Tachard what I had said and got him to translate it into French for the benefit of the Envoys. I could see by their passive faces that they did not believe a word, and nothing would alter their opinion that I did not dare to submit anything to the King any more than I had been prepared to do so during de Chaumont's Embassy.

This neither surprises me nor worries me. I have been in the King's Service for seven years now, and in all that time I have had to deal with men of different nations speaking different tongues and adhering to different beliefs, each and every one with his own aims and personal interests, and to all I have given some measure of Satisfaction, even if it is not always complete, and still maintained my position. No other man in this Kingdom can claim as much.

So, these latest French Envoys will not trouble me. We can settle on a Tacit Disagreement over the question of Narai's conversion.

In a similar way, I ignore la Loubère's repeated complaints that although the French troops have been stationed in the fort at Bangkok, the place has not been ceded to them as a garrison town. With General Desfarges and his men, on the other hand, I endeavour to make myself popular among them, sending gifts and inviting the officers to dine, and be my guests whenever I have time to take the elephant hunt at Louvo. They respond warmly to my courtesies. Desfarges has already been granted a Royal Audience, at which he swore an Oath of Allegiance to King Narai. I now know I have an ally, and can depend on the General's military force to protect me should the need arise. He is often a guest at my house, and although the Envoys disapprove of their officer's conduct, they completely fail in their attempts to sway him against me.

La Loubère is persistent, however, in his demands that Bangkok and Mergui be given over to the French. We have sniped at each other over the past several weeks, and now the argument has boiled over. He told me not to go back on my word, and this implied lack of confidence so angered me that I could not control my temper. He quickly lost his, too, and we became shamefully enmeshed in a heated discourse. Cébéret alone remained calm, and finally persuaded his colleague that the talk was achieving no useful purpose and it would be best if they returned to their lodgings.

42

The issue of Bangkok and Mergui being ceded to the French was never resolved, nor was the rift between Phaulkon and the Envoys, although the Greek had paid the princely sum of 300,000 livres to become a Shareholder in the French Company.

A Treaty was nonetheless concluded and signed on 11th December, 1687. Among its provisions was that the French were permitted to build suitable trading posts and be allowed to enjoy Freedom to Trade subject to the Tariff and to the Right of the King to a selection of such goods as he required. In addition, an island off Mergui was ceded to the French.

Effectively, Cébéret, in taking responsibility for the trade aspects of the French Mission, won no more than had been agreed with Boureau-Deslandes seven years earlier, while la Loubère, in charge of Religious and Political Affairs, received only the scorn of Phaulkon.

After the signing of the Treaty, Cébéret expressed a desire to leave Siam without delay and, receiving the necessary permission, he departed in December, travelling via Mergui where he had arranged for a French vessel to meet him.

In the following two weeks, during which la Loubère remained, his relations with Phaulkon became increasingly bitter. The two avoided each other whenever possible, and on the occasions they did meet, arguments almost inevitably ensued. In particular they argued furiously over a new kind of exploding shell which the French had among their arsenal and which Phaulkon desired to be left behind in Siam for the use of the King's Army. Although la Loubère repeatedly refused to give up the mortars, Phaulkon outwitted him by approaching Desfarges, whom he found was prepared not only to ignore the French Envoy, but to deliver the ordnance to Ayutthaya under his Personal Escort.

As soon as la Loubère heard of this, he knew Phaulkon had got the better of him, and stung at being so outwitted, he ordered his ship to be made ready for his immediate departure. The Greek was surprised at the sudden decision, and scarcely had time to prepare the gifts, including two silver-banded cannons, that Siam was sending to Louis XIV before the Frenchman sailed in early January after a final Audience with the King, during which Narai asked him to convey to Louis his Continuing and Sincere Friendship.

Ayutthaya
3rd February, 1688

Another hot dry season has begun, increasing my annoyance so that I become unbearable both to myself and others. Not that I have any particular target for my Vexation and, indeed, I take certain satisfaction in much that has recently passed.

The second French Embassy, like the first, has Failed in its principle objective. De Chaumont had wanted to convert King Narai to Catholicism; la Loubère and Cébéret wanted control of Bangkok and Mergui. Do I flatter myself if I take credit for Foiling these two Ambitions, both Unacceptable to the Siamese? Or am I to be viewed as an unreliable ally, a man who cannot be trusted, who would bargain away his own mother should it be expedient. I think not.

I know I have been criticized for my arrogance, my sudden bursts of temper, and my tendency to harbour grudges. While regretting these character traits, I do not try to hide them. It is the same with my fondness for luxury and ostentation, which I attribute to the poverty of my youth.

I am puzzled as to why I should have fallen into such a mood of introspection since la Loubère's departure. In part this stems from the death last month of my eldest child, João, which plunged me into the deepest depression and, I fear, clouds my judgement. But my personal loss is compounded by the confusion and ill-will that is the Immediate Legacy of this second French Embassy.

The Treaty I have secured serves our purpose well enough, though there are Decided Weaknesses. Desfarges troops are an inadequate force, while French support is undermined internally by the rift between the French Mission and the Jesuits.

43

Talk of the King's Health was on everyone's lips in the early months of 1688, and rumours of his death circulated prematurely in the bazaars. In truth, he was gravely ill, weakened by an asthmatic cough, although the peoples' fears had been stirred by an Oracle that foretold of Great Upheaval during the transit of the planet Jupiter, expected some time in March or April, talk of which swept through the populace like a river in spate, the flood gates opened by Petracha who urged the Brahmins to make public the Prediction, even to an interpretation of the Upheaval as a Revolution.

The King also put great store by the astrologers and became as much a victim of his superstition as of his asthma.

"It is written in the stars, Constantine," Narai revealed to Phaulkon. "I fear not my own death, but the prediction is of great change in the State of the Realm. That I do fear for my people."

Phaulkon was dismayed at his Protector's weakening spirit, and sought comfort for the King by having a Jesuit Father talk with him, until he realized the folly of his action, which only prompted more rumours, this time that the King was to become a Catholic and dissolve the Buddhist monasteries.

All the while, Petracha remained in the background as the Brahmins spread fear. Unlike his impetuous son, he had never attacked Phaulkon personally, and while he argued at Court against a French presence in the Land, he made it appear that he did so solely as his Duty to his Monarch, and that he himself was disinterested. As he secretly spurred on the Brahmins to spread their Predictions of Doom, he stood in the wings and watched the drama unfold.

Believing the King was close to death, Narai's two brothers, Chao Fa Aphaitot and Chao Fa Noi, who previously had been kept well away from public life, began to give Audiences in Ayutthaya, and several of the Chinese merchants and foreign traders in the Capital had indicated their allegiance to them. Indeed, their following was strong as many regarded them as Heirs to the Throne, yet both were unsuited to rule; Chao Fa, the eldest, being deformed and a drunkard as well, while the younger Chao Fa Noi had been left a deaf mute after the King had had him flogged on suspicion that he had conspired with the Makassars during the rebellion.

A counter force to that of the Princes was posed by Phra Pi, the King's Adopted Son, who although of low birth, had the looks and Manner to carry himself as a High-Born Courtier. He, too, had a popular following as the Heir to the Throne, but his amorous ways with the daughters of several of the Mandarins caused him to be disliked at Court.

Phaulkon had had scant dealing with the Princes, nor was he close to Phra Pi, and consequently he had precious little influence over them. As he now rarely saw the King, he being confined to his sick bed to which only the physicians were admitted, he became vulnerable. Until Narai should fully recover and continue as his

Protector, he had to rely on his wits and the protection of Desfarges' troops. He was nonetheless confident that he could quell any rebellion should it break out with the aid of the superior French arms, and take over the helm of the country until normalcy returned. His one fear was that the French had become undisciplined while idle in Bangkok, and he shuddered whenever he heard reports of their roaming the streets drunk and harassing the people who were already fearful and suspicious.

Louvo
3rd April, 1688

The heat is unbearable, exceptional even for these summer months, and I am sorely oppressed. I have been conducting Petty Affairs of State in the outer courtyard of the Palace, where all daily business is now being done while the King is sick and inaccessible.

In these dangerous times it is essential that I maintain an appearance of Assurance and Dignity. I go about my daily business calmly as if oblivious to the Subversive Air that is all around, spreading its stink equally among commoners and high-born like an Evil Pestilence.

The Palace guard has been strengthened, and throughout the country, between Louvo and Ayutthaya, farmers, boatmen, even the rabble are arming themselves, and this speaks only of fear and rebellion.

44

One of the few Mandarins friendly with Phaulkon called him aside as he entered the Palace outer courtyard. "Lord Wichayen, a word if I may," he said. "I have just come from a brief Audience with the King, and . . ."

"Pray, tell me, how is my Master?" Phaulkon interrupted. "Are there any signs of improvement?"

"Same-same, I am afraid. He is very frail. What ails him more is that he is deeply worried. Worried in particular about you. To ease his mind he has asked me to convey a message to you. It is His Majesty's Feeling that your enemies have become too powerful for you. There is nothing he can do to help you, and he strongly recommends you resign your position and leave the country secretly."

"Resign? I cannot resign so long as my Master is King," Phaulkon replied. "Nor is there any way I will leave secretly, as if slinking away like a mangy dog with its tail between its legs. Nay, Sir. I am most grateful to His Majesty that he should show such concern for me when his mind must be on his Own Recovery, but I have my duty to perform. I cannot, will not desert him."

"Your sentiment reflects well on you, Phaulkon, but perhaps your reasoning is a little muddled by these trying times. You must prepare yourself for the prospect that the King might not recover. He is old and his time must be nigh."

"All the more reason that I must remain at my post. The entire Foreign Course of the Reign is at stake; everything His Majesty has worked towards all these years for the Greater Glory of Siam. I cannot stand by and watch the whole building be razed by fools who are incapable of vision. Narai is the most outward-looking Monarch this country has ever known. Do you not see, we are putting Siam in its rightful place in the world."

Phaulkon was carried away, moved by thoughts of his Master. He had been out under the sun for half the day and perhaps the heat had turned his head, for it was dangerous to talk so openly in the Palace courtyard. No one seemed to have overheard him.

"Please excuse my outburst, I am much disturbed at present," he apologized.

The man lead Phaulkon aside to a quite corner and spoke softly. "Quite, Lord Wichayen. But if I may be truthful with you and offer some friendly advice, let me say that your allegiance to King Narai is honourable, but it is also folly. It is essential to be practical, as I am sure you will appreciate. We Siamese are a fickle people, our hero is our enemy the moment he falls or fails.

"Yes, Narai has been a Great King but his time has passed and his Ideas no longer popular. From the palaces of princes to the hovels of the poorest beggars, you will hear talk of hatred against the foreigners Narai has courted, and even greater hatred for yourself, who many see as our true enemy. I do understand your thinking and I believe you have striven to serve us justly, but sadly there is none who would support you publicly."

The man paused and looked about him to ensure no one was taking undue interest in their conversation.

"There are two parties now vying for the Crown," he continued. "That of the two Princes and that of Phra Pi, the former by far the stronger. Yet both are nothing. The man you must watch is Phra Petracha. He gives face to the Princes, but at the same time he stirs up feeling against the French troops and the missionaries, spreading rumours that the French are plotting to seize the whole country and that you are their Agent. He has already succeeded in rallying a great number of influential people to his side, and it is my guess that he is just biding his time before seizing the Throne for himself."

"Ah, the admirable Phra Petracha. . . . Well, Sir, I thank you kindly for your confidence and advice. I must now hasten to my chambers. There is much to be done. I bid you a good day."

"And you, Lord Wichayen. Please consider carefully what I have said."

Phaulkon took his leave and left the Palace at a normal pace, anxious to give no visible sign of the turmoil he was suffering. He knew he was in a Perilous State, but to be told so was unnerving. Word that the King himself feared for his safety was as unsettling as it was touching.

Walking ahead of his bodyguard, the Greek pondered if his position was as precarious as the Courtier had warned him. He knew what he had been told about Petracha and the fears of the people was true. Only a few days previously, he recalled, Desfarges had visited Ayutthaya, and at the first sight of him the women in the market place flew into a panic and ran away as if the Devil himself was at their heels.

Thus was it easy for Petracha to manipulate the common people and use their fears to his advantage in plotting revolt, though it be treason with the King still alive.

Louvo
7th April, 1688

My fears of Petracha's Treachery are confirmed. This morning I received word that he has taken Official Seals and used them to obtain a supply of arms and powder, which he justifies by saying they are required for the Defence of the King.

I must act quickly and stop this escalation before events overtake me. The only way I can succeed will be in striking at the Legality of Petracha's actions. A personal attack will be fatal, and so I resolve to have him Arrested and Tried for Treason.

To expedite this, I will need the support of the French troops, and I have sent word to Desfarges in Bangkok to join me in Louvo in support of an Action that will be of Service to our respective Monarchs.

45

Desfarges had been awarded the Rank of General only when he was selected to accompany the French Mission to Siam and, with all the enthusiasm of an old man glimpsing late glory, he acted promptly on Phaulkon's call to join him in Louvo. Accompanied by Major de Beauchamp, he travelled without delay to the Summer Capital.

"It's a matter of the utmost importance, and one that need be carried out without hesitation," Phaulkon impressed upon Desfarges after he had told him how he feared Petracha plotted to seize the Throne.

"You realize," he continued, "this means that not only is the King in danger. The whole Royal Family, the French, and the Catholic Religion are all threatened. If we strike at the heart of the plot and take Petracha we shall nip the revolt in the bud and avoid a Catastrophe that would have Disastrous Consequence for us all."

The old General's eyes lit up and he puffed himself up with pride on hearing he was being called to a duty of the Most Profound Importance. "Capital, Sir, capital. I shall be honoured to serve the King and shall myself march at the head of our troops."

"And I, Sir, volunteer to carry out the arrest of this Petracha. Kill him with my own hands if necessary," said Major de Beauchamp, anxious to demonstrate as much Zeal as his commanding officer.

"Thank you, Gentlemen," replied Phualkon. "But let's not be precipitous. We should remain calm and plan carefully. What is imperative, General, is that you return to Bangkok and bring 100 of your troops back to Louvo as soon as possible. It is here that the Revolt is being fermented, and this will remain the centre of the Conspiracy so long as the King is too weak to return to Ayutthaya. But I stress that rumours are rife in the Capital, especially since the King and all the senior Mandarins are here, and so when you pass through Ayutthaya do not give credence to any news you may receive there; it is certain to be false.

"Good luck to you both and God speed."

Louvo
14th April, 1688

That fool Desfarges. I commanded him explicitly not to heed the rumours in Ayutthaya, and what does he do? Precisely what I warned him against.

Once he had reached Bangkok, he lost no time in mustering a force of a hundred hand-picked men and set out immediately on the return journey to Louvo. As he approached Ayutthaya, the sight of his troops sent the people of the outlying villages into panic—men, women, and children screaming and fleeing in all directions as if the enemy was at the city gates.

Startled and confused as to why these ordinary Siamese should act as if he were about to attack, Desfarges halted his men and sent one of his officers into the city to try to discover what had triggered the Commotion. Joining a throng of people in one of the bazaars, the officer heard news that the King was dead. No one seemed to doubt it, and there was talk of rioting and looting in Louvo, which they said had been thrown into Chaos.

Uncertain what to believe, the officer called on the Governor of Ayutthaya, told him of his Royal Mission, and asked if it was true that the King had died. The Governor assured him the rumours were false, Narai still lived and all was calm in Louvo.

Perhaps distrustful of the news brought by his officer, Desfarges was not convinced and decided to probe further, choosing to consult, of all people, M. Véret.

I have previously warned him to be wary of Véret. The man is a Scoundrel and a Thief, forging his accounts and stealing from the French Company. I am wise to his tricks, though choose not to expose him, and he is thus afraid of me and seeks every opportunity to Discredit me so that should I inform the Company of his irregularities they will be the less likely to believe me.

When Desfarges met him, Véret must have seen another chance to do me a Disservice, and told the General that the rumours were true, that Narai was dead, that I had been arrested, and Louvo was in the hands of rebels. To convince the General further, he took him across the river to see the French missionaries—who are equally wary of me—and they confirmed what Véret had said.

Ever cautious, Desfarges found himself in a quandary, and delayed over what action he should take. Every moment's delay puts me in Increasing Danger; I cannot act against Petracha without the support of the French, but the longer I wait the stronger he becomes.

Finally, the General decided to dispatch one of his lieutenants to Louvo to discover the truth of the situation, while he remained with his troops in Ayutthaya.

This officer, Lieutenant Leroy by name, from whom I learnt of Desfarges' fears and hesitation, now of course finds everything normal and peaceful here. I assured him the King was still alive, and then sent two of my secretaries to take him around the city, including the Palace, so he could see for himself that there was no cause for alarm.

Once the lieutenant had satisfied himself that the rumours being spread abroad in Ayutthaya were false, I urged him to return immediately to the Capital, and gave him a letter for Desfarges, in which I explained that the King is alive but that I most urgently require the French in Louvo, where he should proceed without delay.

I still have confidence in Desfarges. He might be old and more cautious than I would wish, but he allied himself with me against la Loubère and Cébéret and I count him as my Friend and Ally.

46

After days of waiting for the arrival of Desfarges and his troops, Phaulkon suffered bitter disappointment and deep hurt when a certain Captain d'Assieu arrived at Louvo alone and bearing a letter from his General.

Phaulkon ripped the seal off the paper and read its contents with disbelief:

"After consultation with Monsieur Véret and the Abbé de Lionne, and given the Prevailing Climate of Uncertainty throughout the country," Desfarges wrote, "I have decided to order my men back to Bangkok. For the moment I shall stay at Ayutthaya where I do beseech you, for both your sake and mine, that you join me so that we might offer our Combined Support to the two Princes."

Louvo
1st May, 1688

Is there no more loyalty in this world? Am I always to be betrayed by knaves and fools? I am de facto the First Minister of this country, the Most Trusted Advisor to the King, and I have pursued the goals set by him Faithfully and to the best of my ability.

I am known and respected in the Royal Courts of England and France, as well as in the Vatican. I have negotiated Treaties of far-reaching import for Siam and its future as a Kingdom of Power and Wealth. I have shown more loyalty and less self interest than any of the Highest-Ranking Officials of Europe and Siam who have shared the stage with me in this Comic Drama of lust, greed, and deceit. My fault as a player has been not to see the comedy, a comedy of errors which others will call Diplomacy. Have I reached this far only to be let down by fools?

In spite of my letter delivered into his hands by Lieutenant Leroy, Desfarges has chosen to desert me. His courage may have failed him, though I believe his mind has been Poisoned against me by the wretched Abbé de Lionne at the French Mission in Ayutthaya. The priest has never tried to hide his Animosity towards the Jesuits, and by going against me he undermines their influence. My guess is that he, along with Véret, has convinced Desfarges that if he comes to my aid, the Siamese will identify him as my ally, which will bring down a Backlash against all the Frenchmen in Siam. Whereas the fool cannot see that if I fail, the French are doomed anyway; only if I remain in power will the Interests of France have a champion. It is all I have been working for these past three years.

47

On the day following receipt of Desfarges' missive, Phaulkon had recovered sufficient calm to call on Captain d'Assieu before the latter returned to Ayutthaya.

"Captain, it is imperative that I understand fully your General's reasoning. Pray tell me all that happened before you were sent here with his letter."

"With respect, Monsieur Phaulkon," the officer replied, "Monsieur Véret and the Abbé de Lionne have convinced General Desfarges that you seek his military support only in order to increase your own standing at Court."

"What! That cannot be so."

"Again, with respect, Sir, the talk is that Phra Petracha has approached you, saying that he proposed to join Phra Pi against the Princes, whom he intended to arrest and charge with treason, and then raise an armed force and place the Crown on whose head he should choose. He is supposed to have said that that head could be yours as he only looks for rest and retirement."

"And those idiots believe that? It is true that Petracha did approach me, but do not Véret and the others understand that I merely let Petracha play into my hands by exposing his plans. Did the rumours not include what I replied to Petracha, that no levy of troops could be made unless Sanctioned by the King? Can they not credit the confusion, the complexity of intrigue . . ." Phaulkon threw up his arms in despair, bitter at how easily Desfarges, de Lionne, and Véret could abandon him at what they must realize was the most critical juncture in his entire life.

"Talk is useless. . . . Captain, you will take my orders to your General that regardless of whatever rumours he has heard, I command him again to bring his force to Louvo immediately and without fail."

Louvo
15th May, 1688

I have received a final reply from Desfarges. It confirms my Worst Fears. He says that while the death of King Narai is being reported throughout the Land, he cannot justify re-deploying his troops and deserting the fortress at Bangkok. He concludes by offering me a retreat with him and his family.

The trembling in my hands and body became so violent that I was forced to sit. For how long I do not know I stared at the walls, the Persian tapestry covering it unseen in my eyes as my mind swam in a mire of bitterness and sorrow. Never since the time I was shipwrecked off the Southern Shores and stripped bare by bandits have I suffered such despair, or felt so naked. At that time, as I huddled among the bushes hiding my shame I had thought it preferable to take my own life than to face failure. Then, I remembered, as soon as I was face to face with my enemy, the Governor of Ligor, I had shed my despair as a snake sloughs its skin, and became determined to fight his Accusations. With that thought and an acceptance that I am abandoned, I was able to steady my mind.

Suddenly the room resumed its familiar splendour and I saw afresh the rich colours of the tapestry, the intricate mother-of-pearl inlay of the Chinese furniture, and the lacquered brilliance of the Japanese screens. The gold of the candlesticks shone once more, their encrusted rubies and sapphires winking at me. I saw my life as richer, more glorious than these trappings of my success; success I have won through Defiance, a refusal to give in.

If I accept Desfarges' offer to take refuge with him and his family in Bangkok, I will abandon not just the riches of my life, but that very life itself. Should I remain at Louvo and face my enemies, all the wealth and success of my life will remain even though I should die because I have not abandoned them. What I have achieved, for which the material objects are but the symbols, will not die. History will know me. But as a pathetic refugee cowering beneath Desfarges' coat-tails, history would Damn me as a Coward. I will fight and I could well yet win. That Fate might be against me means that maybe Fate is still with me. It will suffice. It is my Destiny.

As I regained a sense of calm, an idea has formed whereby I may still be able to thwart the scheming of Petracha, even without the assistance of Desfarges' force. I will need to gain an Audience with Narai, which since his illness has been rarely granted.

While planning this action, my conscience was troubled by the thought of Maria. I cannot have spoken more than a few passing words to her during the past troubled days, preoccupied as I am with events in Louvo and my attempts to secure Desfarges' support. We have always talked freely about our desires and our cares, but more than our closeness, I value Maria's patience with my unpredictable humours and her understanding—most unusual for a woman—of Affairs of State.

But for all her accomplishments and love, Maria remains an enigma to me. I give her beautiful and valuable gifts, and a life that many a princess would envy, yet I know none of these things truly matter to her, the same as they by themselves are nought to me. But

I sustain myself with the Duty I feel bound to; she has but me, and I will say in honesty I cannot think myself as anything but the most difficult person with whom to partner. Still she stays by my side, even now when the threat to our lives could so easily be avoided should we flee. I can only imagine that her Love of God, through which she gives her love to me, allows her to bear the many burdens of our lives. If I love her for her charm and intelligence, I worship her for her loyalty. In that alone do I find true meaning.

Our son Jorge worries me more. He is an innocent, and if he should suffer because of the action I feel bound to take, it would be brought on him solely by myself. It is possible that Maria, at my urging, would take him to safety in Bangkok? My course of action, however, must be decided by my Own Reasons, however selfish they may appear—for if I choose to run away, my son will no longer have a True Father as I would have denied myself. I am no judge as to whether such an argument is philosophically acceptable, but it is the only one I can accept.

I believe the crisis facing King Narai and the Fate of Siam transcends personal considerations, and life and death are not the True Stakes in this game of chance. To abandon my Royal Master, who has always shown me the Greatest Friendship and tenderness, and leave him defenseless against his enemies would be to deny all that I have made of my life. If I desert him now, history would know me only as an opportunist, blown by the wind and not driven by a pure Zeal.

After these musings, my spirits are much revived. I have always been a man who sets my course and refuses to veer one way or the other no matter what contrary winds should blow. However rough the sea might become, I would lash myself to the helm and never diverge a Single Degree off the chosen compass bearing. Now it is a question of what that course should be. Is there a way in which I could spike Petracha's guns and Retain my Own Power?

Securing an appropriate succession to the Throne appears to me the obvious way of defusing the situation. The difficulty will be to persuade Narai to name a successor. He has no legitimate son and heir, although primogenitor does not necessarily secure succession in Siam, where a Council may appoint the monarch if there is no clear line of succession. But Narai does have a daughter. Admittedly there have been no precedents for this, although strong and powerful queens have sometimes in the past been near equals to their Royal Spouses.

48

The female guards at the inner court of the Palace refused to admit Phaulkon, though they allowed him to send in a message to his personal attendants, who graciously granted him a few minutes at the King's bedside.

It was the first time he had seen Narai in many weeks, and he was shocked at the sight of his Protector frail and weak, his breath shallow and laboured. At first he feared the King would not recognize him, or be unable to speak, but presently Narai opened his eyes and whispered a greeting to his Favourite.

He took a sip from the cup of Chinese tea an attendant held out to him and, beckoning Phaulkon to come closer, Narai beseeched the Greek to flee from Louvo, leave Siam, and seek refuge in France.

Phaulkon replied that his own safety was of no matter, it was the Peace and Security of Siam that was at stake. He humbly suggested that until the King should recover from his illness, he should name a successor, for whom he suggested his daughter, so that the fear and uncertainty of the people may be allayed. Hearing this, Narai raised himself up on his pillows and refused the suggestion. The energy he summoned was too much, and he collapsed back onto his bed, unable to explain his decision, nor tell what he proposed for the Future of his Kingdom.

Seeing there was no more to be done, Phaulkon was about to take his leave when he heard a commotion in the outer chambers, above which sounded the angered voice of Petracha. With fear in their eyes, the attendants ushered the Greek to the back of the chamber and hid him behind a screen, begging him not to move nor utter a sound no matter what might happen.

One of the servants then went outside and was away some minutes before returning in a state of near panic. He knelt by Narai's bed and reported in a hurried whisper that Petracha had come into the Palace and was meeting various Mandarins and military men, seemingly in Secret Consultation. No one had hindered Petracha's movements within the Palace; none of the guards had either the courage or the will to resist.

Narai drew on all the strength he could muster to hear and understand what he was being told. His eyes bulged in disbelief as his tired mind comprehended the full truth that Petracha, his childhood friend and trusted military officer, was plotting against him. Faith in friendship died within him, and he ordered Petracha be arrested, but there was no one who could carry out the command.

Suddenly the noise outside grew louder and the doors to the King's bedroom were flung open. Petracha entered the chamber accompanied by three of his followers. Each had a sword in hand. Fitter than a man half his 55 years, Petracha, standing there amid the brocades and silks of the opulent furnishings, was a threatening figure.

No one spoke for several moments, and the room was charged with the mixed emotions of the servants' terror and the old King's outrage. Raising himself up from his bed, Narai called for his sword, and then quivering with anger and the exertion of standing, he challenged Petracha. But the effort was again too much. Before he could even curse his former friend, he collapsed again. Petracha and his men stared at the old man, then slowly sheathed their swords and turned to leave the room. Only then did Petracha speak:

"My apologies. I mean you no harm. Only I had been informed that Phaulkon the Greek was here, and I believe he is a Danger to Siam."

Showing no emotion, Petracha bowed and withdrew without a further word. Whether he had second thoughts at the last minute, or whether he was satisfied there was time enough for the King to die a natural death, Phaulkon could not tell.

Louvo
16th May, 1688

Today I saw with my own eyes Petracha come to threaten the King. He did nothing when he saw the old man exhausted, but while he may have stayed his hand for the moment, rebellion is in his heart. Perhaps it was a fatal delay. Perhaps there is still time for me to counter-attack and arrest Petracha now that I have seen him in his true colours.

Just an hour ago, a messenger reported to me that Phra Pi has been tricked by a group of military officers into leaving Narai's Private Quarters at the Palace. There has been no news of him since, and the only possible interpretation of his disappearance is that he will be Murdered. I do not doubt it; when succession to the Throne is disputed, it is common among the Siamese for potential but unpopular heirs to be Ruthlessly Eliminated. At this news, I am certain Petracha will shortly move to seize power. If Phra Pi is dead, and the two Princes in Ayutthaya too ineffectual to be counted, there is nothing to stop him. Only I stand in his way.

There is nothing more I can do save stand fast to my Duty and trust in God that he may give me the strength and wisdom to take whatever action opens to me to quell unrest and avert a Revolution that I fear is imminent.

Epilogue
Louvo
18th May and
the days following, 1688

The sun was directly overhead and Phaulkon cast no shadow *as he strode purposefully towards the Palace. His eyes were alert, darting from side to side, but now, past the market, the streets were deserted as was usual for the hottest hours of the day, and no one blocked his path. He was confident even though he knew his bodyguard was pathetically small, but he had always reckoned a European fighting man worth a score of Siamese soldiers. His plan was to join the King, fighting his way though the Palace courtyards if necessary, and make his stand by His Majesty's side as a loyal servant and True Defender of the Present and Rightful Ruler of Siam. He thought nothing of the French, of the grandiose schemes he had long plotted for Siam. Today his duty was simple.*

The tall main gates of the Palace stood open and unguarded. Phaulkon believed Petracha had yet to act and secure the Palace with his own supporters. His confidence grew. He passed though the gate unchallenged. Suddenly, from behind the huge wooden doors, where they had been waiting, a troop of Siamese soldiers swarmed around Phaulkon and his men. Still he showed no fear, nor panic. But they were so outnumbered that no amount of Valour could serve them, and within minutes Phaulkon was bloodied and beaten. His companions were disarmed but not ill-treated, while he, Lord Wichayen, Phaulkon the Greek was taken prisoner and bound with heavy chains in the very Palace courtyard where not so long ago, at a time of personal triumph, he escorted the Embassies of France amid the Greatest Ceremony.

Only a short distance away, Lady Phaulkon had remained in the chapel of their home. She was praying for her husband's safety, fearful, hopeful, watchful, her Faith in her God so much greater than her belief in the loyalty of Lord Phaulkon's bodyguard. Her apprehension became too much and she prepared to go herself to the Palace when the door of the chapel was thrust open as a servant rushed in and threw himself at her feet. His weeping and simultaneous gasps to catch his breath made his words inaudible until Lady Phaulkon calmed him.

"Your husband, My Lady, he is attacked and killed," the servant uttered at last.

Lady Phaulkon stood motionless, her eyes closed as she struggled to comprehend what she heard. It could not be true. It seemed to her only moments earlier that Phaulkon was there with her, kissing her cheek. It could not be true. Not her beloved Constantine, the man who in the past had overcome so much.

A pounding at the gate and the sounds of a crowd entering the gardens brought her to her senses. She ran to the room of her son and swept up the four-year-old into her protective arms. With the boy still clutched to her chest, she entered the reception chamber where an officer awaited her.

"Lady Phaulkon, I am sent by Lord Petracha who wishes you to know that he intends no harm should come to you or your child. He informs that a guard shall be placed at your gates for your protection."

"But my husband, Lord Phaulkon? What of he? Is he dead?"

The officer refused to answer, and from his silence Maria knew that Constantine must still be alive. She implored the man to give her news, to tell her where her husband was being confined, but the officer only bowed at the distraught woman and left the house without saying a word more. She was left alone with her child, gladdened to believe that her husband was still alive but fearful should he be imprisoned. "What sorrows have befallen us?" she whispered to her son as she walked unsteadily back to the chapel. Prayer was her only refuge.

The somberness of Phaulkon's house was mocked by the mood of rejoicing outside in the streets of Louvo. Word that Petracha had assumed power and his authority was recognized by the Mandarins now that King Narai was ailing and not expected to live much longer spread rapidly throughout the town.

At all levels of society the news was received with equal relief: the Mandarins were pleased with Petracha's Patriotism and desire to rid the country of foreigners, the Buddhist priests were thankful for a man they saw as a Restorer of the True Religion, and the people were happy with the novelty of succession.

No one, high or low, considered for a moment that Petracha was a Usurper. All rejoiced in the downfall of Phaulkon.

"There, I told you so," the fat old woman in the orange and green sarong gloated to her niece. Told you that that Lord Wichayen's for the chop. Got him in irons I hear, in the gaol of the Palace. That's the last we'll see of him, believe me. It's a blessing."

"I don't know, Auntie. I don't understand it all."

The two women were bathing in the river only a short distance downstream from the Palace. The sun was low in the sky, its slanting rays shone softly through the branches of the trees on the opposite bank, and an air of calm descended over the town.

"I tell you it's saved a lot of trouble. Nothing good was going to come of them foreigners. Their's ain't our way of things. Never were, never will be. I don't understand all that talk of Christianity, but I know it's not right. You know yourself the bad feeling that's been about these last few months. No, folks ain't been them usual selves. It's been unsettling, not normal."

"I know what you mean," said the younger woman climbing out of the water and onto the bank where she slipped a clean sarong over her head and demurely removed the wet one she bathed in. "But I thought Phaulkon was a proud, handsome, and brave man who understood our ways like no other foreigner ever has, and I've heard said he wanted nothing but the Glory of Siam as our beloved King had."

"And how do you, my little market seller, know what our King has desired? Your head's just full of romantic dreams, turned by the sight of all these fancy foreigners swaggering hither and thither. Come on, its getting dark."

ф

Phaulkon lay on the mud floor of the gaol, though that was too grand a name for the pit and fence of wooden stakes in which he was penned like an animal. He had been stripped of the chains in which he was brought there, though his hands were still shackled, and stripped too of the embroidered jacket and lace-trimmed shirt, his breeches and his leather boots, so he was reduced to near nakedness. His gaoler and inquisitor dragged him to a corner where a wood fire blazed with irons lying in the heart of the heat. Phaulkon was thrown on his back, and as the gaoler clasped his legs in his muscular arms, the inquisitor removed one of the irons from the fire and lays it across the soles of Phaulkon's feet.

Phaulkon's screams were dying on the air when the inquisitor spoke. "You are a traitor. You plotted to sell Siam to the French. Confesss."

Phaulkon said nothing. More irons were pulled from the fire, the wretched screams renewed as the pain increased and the smell of burning flesh hung in the still night air.

The urge to confess was strong in Phaulkon's mind, if only it would stop the pain. Yet greater than the physical pain was the shame and humiliation he felt, and the little part of his brain still not twisted by the Agony of his Body told him that in confessing to lies, to acts he did not commit, nor thoughts held, he would suffer more in the defeat than in any torture.

ф

Two days passed, days of burning and beatings, no water nor food was brought to Phaulkon until his wife, learning of his place of imprisonment, was allowed to bring him a little sustenance. Even this was soon stopped when, on 1st June, Petracha was told of the enormous wealth Phaulkon was said to have amassed, and sent to his house an officer and 100 soldiers who carried away all furniture, money, jewels, and everything else of any conceivable value.

Maria burst into tears at the sight of her home being ransacked and cried, "What have I done to be treated like a criminal?"

Two Jesuit fathers consoled her, and once she was composed she remarked more to herself than to any listener, "God gave all; he takes all away. His holy name be praised. God alone is left to us and none can separate us from Him. I pray only for my husband's deliverance."

ф

There was no respite. It was six o' clock the same evening when the Siamese officer returned to the house and demanded Lady Phaulkon hand over her husband's hidden treasure, reputed to be fabulous.

"There is no hidden treasure," she said. "I have hidden nothing. If you doubt my word, look for yourself. You are master of this house now."

"No! I do not seek. You will bring it, or I will have you beaten." The officer beckoned to his men who advanced on Maria and threatened her with the thick rattan canes they carried.

"Have mercy on me, please!" pleaded Maria as the men bound her and tied her to the door. She was confused; there was no hidden treasure, but the officer lost patience and commanded her flogged. Her arms, hands, and fingers were beaten mercilessly, and although her grandmother, relatives, and servants threw themselves at the officer's feet begging he stop, the torture continued for two hours.

Finally, Maria was carried away half dead from her sufferings. No hidden treasure was ever found in Phaulkon's house.

ф

Four more day passed and Petracha realized that if his greed was not to be assuaged by hidden treasure, his hatred could be fed by the death of Phaulkon.

It was six o'clock in the evening on 5th June, 1688. A crier mounted the platform in the outer courtyard of the Palace and publically announced that Constantine Phaulkon had been convicted of treason for being in league with the enemy, and his execution ordered. There was no trial; only a sentence of death.

ϕ

Darkness was falling as the Palace gates swung open and Phaulkon, under heavy guard, was brought forth on the back of an elephant.

A gasp of surprise was audible from the crowd.

"Is that him? Can't be," asked the fat market vendor who had joined the crowd with her niece after hearing news of the crier's proclamation. "Why, he was a well-set man, powerful and well fleshed. Look at that, worse than a ghost."

The niece said nothing but stared up as the man passed by. His body was thin and twisted, his cheeks sunken, and agony was written in every line of his ashen face, telling of the tortures he had borne. His eyes, however, burned with the same Fire as ever. He looked straight ahead holding his head high. In a calm voice he was heard uttering his prayers.

The procession headed towards the forest of Tale Chupsorn, but soldiers barred the public from following this squalid night-time execution. At a clearing the chief executioner called a halt. Phaulkon was helped down from the elephant and was told to ready himself. He stood alone, calm as he prepared to meet finally his Destiny. He was ruined, reviled. He was Unrepentant save only to his God.

Slowly he knelt, placed his hands together in silent prayer, so moving to behold that his executioners would tell of it afterwards to their families. His prayers finished, Phaulkon rose and lifted his hands towards the black sky and looked directly at the officer in charge.

"I am innocent," he said in a steady voice. "I die with a Clear Conscience, knowing that I have loyally served my God and my King, and all my efforts have been directed towards my adopted country, Siam. I forgive my enemies as I trust to be forgiven by God.

"Were I as guilty as my enemies declare me, my wife and son are innocent. I commend them to your protection, asking for them neither wealth nor position, but only life and liberty."

So saying, Phaulkon took from his pocket the cross of the Order of St. Michel, given by the King of France, as a reward or as a bribe it mattered not then; it was accepted in good faith. He handed this to the officer, asking that it be given to his son.

Phaulkon turned and saw Luang Sorasak standing close by the swordsman. He smiled and knelt, holding his body erect, his eyes to the heavens, appearing at peace.

He crossed himself and was then motionless as the swordsman stepped forward.

Acknowledgements

I am indebted to the following authors and their books for information, ideas, images, and quotations, without which *Falcon* could not have been written:

Luang Sitsayamkan, *The Greek Favourite of the King of Siam*;
E. W. Hutchinson, *Adventurers in Siam in the 17th Century*;
Maurice Collis, *Siamese White;*
Fr. de Béze (ed. E. W. Hutchinson), *1688 Revolution in Siam*;
Guy Tachard, *A Relation of the Voyage to Siam*;
Abbé de Choisy (trans. Michael Smithies), *Journal of a Voyage to Siam, 1685-1686*;
Michael Smithies (ed.), *The Chevalier de Chaumont and The Abbé de Choisy: Aspects of the Embassy to Siam, 1685*;
Count Claude de Forbin (ed. Michael Smithies), *The Siamese Memoirs of Count Claude de Forbin, 1685-1688*;

Simon de la Loubère, *A New Historical Relation of the Kingdom of Siam*;

Nicolas Gervaise, *The Natural and Political History of the Kingdom of Siam*;

Michael Smithies, *A Resounding Failure: Martin and the French in Siam, 1672-1693*.

Special thanks are due to Mr. Michael Smithies who kindly read the manuscript and provided expert historical advice; any mistakes are mine and not his.

My thanks also to Asia Books' editor Richard Baker for his support and many helpful insights.